Informal Assessments for
Fluency Development

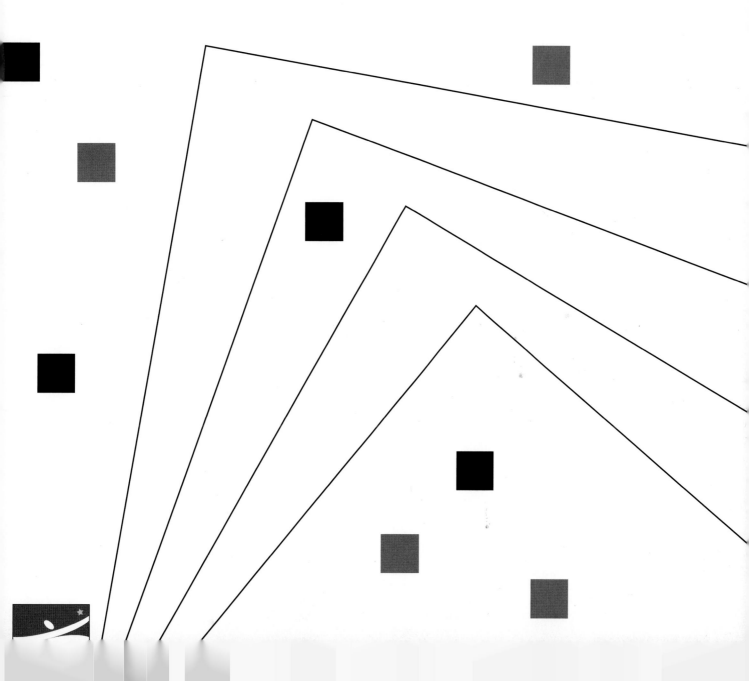

Benchmark Education Company
629 Fifth Avenue Pelham, NY 10803
www.benchmarkeducation.com

ISBN: 978-1-4509-2883-0

For ordering information, call Toll-Free 1-877-236-2465 or visit our Web site: www.benchmarkeducation.com.

Informal Assessments for Fluency Development

Table of Contents

Benchmark EDUCATION
Building Literacy for Life™

Assessment Introduction

Daily teaching goes hand in hand with ongoing assessment and evaluation. The wide variety of reading, writing, spelling, and language assessments provided by Benchmark Education Company enables teachers to:

- obtain multiple perspectives on the literacy growth occurring in their classrooms;
- monitor and reflect on their teaching and students' learning;
- make informed decisions about students' progress and needs;
- select appropriate materials and instructional techniques that match students' current level of development;
- document progress over time through a cumulative portfolio;
- report progress to students, parents, and administrators.

Meaningful, ongoing, and multifaceted observation is the heart of the evaluation process. Since observations must occur in authentic contexts, utilize your small-group reading time to document students' efforts to join discussions; ask and answer questions; react to prompts; contribute ideas for graphic organizers; process text; problem-solve new words; apply targeted skills and strategies, and act out and/or talk, draw, or write about books.

The integration of assessment, teaching, and learning supports effective literacy instruction. Benchmark Education Company provides teachers with the tools for understanding and documenting literacy development. Teachers can use this information to differentiate instruction by developmental reading behaviors and characteristics, metacognitive and comprehension strategy needs, instructional reading levels, fluency, and vocabulary understandings.

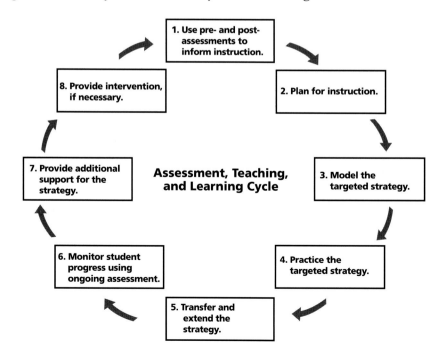

Assessment, Teaching, and Learning Cycle

1. Use pre- and post-assessments to inform instruction.
2. Plan for instruction.
3. Model the targeted strategy.
4. Practice the targeted strategy.
5. Transfer and extend the strategy.
6. Monitor student progress using ongoing assessment.
7. Provide additional support for the strategy.
8. Provide intervention, if necessary.

Rhodes and Shanklin (1993) outline the eleven principles of literacy assessment. Each of these principles is supported in every Benchmark Education Company assessment product.

11 Principles of Literacy Assessment	How BEC Assessment Tools Support the Principles
1. Assess authentic reading and writing.	A variety of ongoing informal assessment tools are available for use before, during, and after literacy instruction.
2. Assess reading and writing in a variety of contexts.	Assessment tools can be administered one-on-one, in small groups, or with the whole class.
3. Assess the literacy environment, instruction, and students.	Assessment tools prompt teacher reflection and provide direction on linking assessment results to instruction.
4. Assess processes as well as products.	Rubrics and assessment tools are available for lesson analysis and noting observable developmental behaviors and characteristics.
5. Analyze error patterns in reading and writing.	Oral reading records and rubrics identify error patterns, strengths, and needs.
6. Consider background knowledge in the assessment of reading and writing.	Student interest questionnaires and surveys gain insight into a students' literacy background and understandings.
7. Base assessment on normal developmental patterns and behavior in reading and writing.	A variety of reading behaviors and characteristics checklists are available to assist in noting developmental milestones and then reporting and planning during assessment meetings.
8. Clarify and use standards in the assessment of reading and writing.	Assessments are aligned with National Literacy Standards and state expectations for learning.
9. Use triangulation to corroborate data and make decisions.	Multiple assessments target different areas of literacy development and are designed to facilitate triangulation of data.
10. Involve students, parents, and other school personnel in the assessment process.	Sharing results from the Benchmark Education Assessments in data team meetings and parent conferences informs and involves others in the process of linking assessment and instruction.
11. Make assessment an ongoing part of everyday reading and writing opportunities and instruction.	Each assessment book provides guidance on how to schedule, manage, organize, and store assessments. Calendars and other planning tools are also provided.

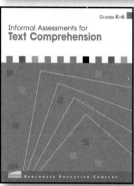

Benchmark Education Company Assessment

The Benchmark Education Company Assessment resources provide tools for ongoing literacy assessments. Each resource has a variety of planning and assessment tools that can be used to inform instruction. Assessment resources can be administered to the whole group, small group, or individual students.

Informal Assessments for Reading Development

- tools for documenting reading behaviors over time, acquisition of concepts about print, and English-language development
- oral reading records
- prompting guides
- reading conference note-taking forms that focus on characteristics of reading development

Informal Assessments for Text Comprehension

- tools for assessing metacognitive and comprehension strategy understandings
- tools for genre and text structure retellings
- comprehension prompting guides
- reading conference note-taking forms that focus on comprehension strategy development

Informal Assessments for Fluency Development

- tools for assessing accuracy, rate, prosody, and oral reading performances
- prompting guides
- reading conference note-taking forms that focus on fluency development

Informal Assessments for Vocabulary Development

- tools for assessing Tier One, Two, and Three vocabulary understandings
- prompting guides
- reading conference note-taking forms that focus on vocabulary development

Informal Assessments for Writing Development

- tools for assessing writing development
- rubric and checklists for assessing genre and text structure
- writing conference note-taking forms

Scheduling, Managing, Organizing, and Storing Assessments

Documenting progress through a cumulative portfolio is one of the greatest advantages of classroom-based assessment. Following are some tips to carry out this process in a teacher- and student-friendly manner.

Scheduling Assessments

Use some assessments as pre- and post-evaluations of growth and development, completing them at the beginning and end of the school year. Conduct other assessments on a more frequent basis as needed. Assess informally during literacy activities every day. Schedule an individual literacy conference with each student every month, and use the information in instructional planning. Hold additional reading and writing conferences as needed to meet students' immediate needs, allowing students to schedule conferences with you as well. Assess students in greatest need of intervention or additional instructional support more frequently—every one to two weeks.

Planning Calendars

Planning calendars help teachers schedule and manage assessments throughout the school year. Teachers can use the masters in the Appendix to note key dates for administering and gathering assessment data for an entire class or individual students.

Year-at-a-Glance Planning Calendar Record state, district, and classroom scheduled assessment dates. (See Appendix page 112)

Month-at-a-Glance Planning Calendar Record progress-monitoring assessments for the entire class or 1–3 students per day. (See Appendix page 113)

Week-at-a-Glance Planning Calendar Record progress-monitoring assessments and individual reading conferences for the week. (See Appendix page 114)

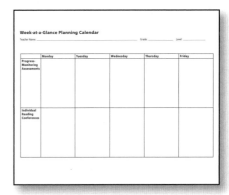

Managing Assessments

Start with one assessment tool and gradually build to the desired collection, as indicated in the following implementation steps.

1. Organize your classroom learning environment. Establish consistent routines and clear expectations for a variety of instructional settings, including whole-group, small-group, and independent activities.

2. Create a management system and schedule for administering formal and informal assessment measures. Identify a simple storage and retrieval system. Set a manageable schedule.

3. Start slowly and proceed one student at a time until all are assessed and you have identified their literacy developmental stages, strengths, and needs.

4. Create class profiles of your findings to serve as a lesson-planning reference and cumulative documentation of growth. Update the profile with each month's individual student conference data.

5. Reflect on the information gathered:

    Are students progressing in a timely fashion?

    What is their overall growth during a specified time frame?

    Are your goals for students being met?

    Is your assessment informing instruction and vice versa?

    Do you see transfer of the skills, strategies, and behaviors you have modeled and taught?

    Do the students in your class reflect the national standards and expectations for their grade level?

Organizing and Storing Assessment Materials

A simple plan for collecting and retrieving each type of record will ensure success and ongoing implementation.

Color code and use separate pocket folders or three-ring binders for each aspect of literacy to be assessed. Have a clearly identified and labeled location to house the individual student assessment folders or binders. Within each folder or binder, use dividers and pockets to store the completed individual assessment tools and work samples.

Store the completed group profile charts in lesson-planning books or create a separate three-ring binder. The binder can serve as an instructional reference tool and cumulative documentation of teaching and learning. Use index tab dividers to note the different profile charts to be collected and used over a school year. Include national, state, and district grade-level recommendations and expectations to complete this instructional reference binder.

Observations and Responsive Teaching

Daily observations of students engaged in meaningful literacy experiences provide detailed information regarding literacy development, strengths, and needs. Documenting observations on a regular basis provides opportunities for teachers to reflect on instruction and areas in need of further assessment. Tomlinson & McTighe remind us that "Responsive teaching suggests a teacher will make modifications in how students get access to important ideas and skills, in ways that students make sense of and demonstrate essential ideas and skills, and in the learning environment—all with an eye to supporting maximum success for each learner." Observations of student learning and transfer provide the link between the assessment and instruction process.

Anecdotal Notes

Anecdotal notes are the observations that are written by the teacher during or after a literacy event. These detailed notes capture students' processing behaviors so they may be further analyzed and used to inform the next instructional move. Anecdotal notes can be taken in whole- or small-group settings or for individuals. These informal notes contain valuable information about students' strengths, weaknesses, progress, needs, processing abilities, or any other observations teachers feel are significant.

Use the Anecdotal Notes master (Appendix page 115) to record notes and observations. Place one small sticky note in each box (one per student). After recording the student's name, date, and your observations, transfer the sticky notes to individual students' portfolios.

What Research Says About Fluency Assessment

"Fluency combines accuracy, automaticity, and oral reading prosody, which taken together, facilitate the reader's construction of meaning. It is demonstrated during oral reading through ease of word recognition, appropriate pacing, phrasing, and intonation. It is a factor in both oral and silent reading that can limit or support comprehension."

—Kuhn, Schwanenflugel, Meisinger, 2010

Reading fluency is best described as the ability to read texts quickly, accurately, and with appropriate expression. Many educators, unfortunately, do not have the tools to teach this vital skill, and many who do teach fluency may not observe and record their students' progress. This book is designed to specifically address this need, and to help teachers facilitate fluency assessment.

Reading fluency should be assessed on a regular basis largely because fluency is considered as an essential characteristic of a proficient reader (National Reading Panel, 2001). The ongoing monitoring of oral reading fluency allows the teacher to monitor and benchmark student progress over time. Ongoing fluency assessments (informal, teacher observations, and formal assessments) also enable educators to determine whether instructional goals have been met.

Research About Fluency Assessment & Instruction*	How *Informal Assessments for Fluency Development* Supports Best Practices
Automatic word recognition is central to the construct of fluency and fluency's role in the comprehension of text (Samuels, 2004, 2006). Processes are considered to be automatic when they possess four properties: speed, effortlessness, autonomy, and lack of conscious awareness (Logan, 1997). Whether developed through repetition or the wide reading of texts, automaticity occurs on multiple levels and connects to comprehension in multiple ways (Samuels, 2004, Logan, 1997).	Tools for one-minute timed readings, lists of high-frequency word phrases, rubrics, and checklists help teachers identify word recognition and decoding automaticity.
A critical component of reading fluency is the ability to read with prosody; that is, with appropriate expression or intonation coupled with phrasing that allows for the maintenance of meaning (Cowie, Douglas-Cowie, & Wichmann, 2002; Miller & Schwanenflugel, 2006, 2008; Schwanenflugel, Hamilton, Kuhn, Wisenbaker & Stahl, 2004). Prosody captures the rise and falls of pitch, rhythm, and stress-the pausing, lengthening, and elision surrounding certain words and phrases that is found in the pull of linguistic communication (Hirschberg, 2002).	Fluency checklists, rubrics, and self-assessments identify specific elements of prosody and the integration with word recognition, accuracy, and rate while reading.
The most important characteristic of the fluent reader is the ability to decode and to comprehend the text at the same time and other characteristics of fluency such as accuracy of word recognition, speed of reading, and the ability to read orally with expression simply serve as indicators that fluency has been achieved (Samuels, 2006). Skilled reading is a complicated act that requires the coordination of input from multiple sources, including syntactic knowledge, orthographic knowledge, and affective factors among others that allows the reader to construct meaning from text. (McKenna & Stahl, 2003, RAND Reading Study Group, 2002)	Comprehension questions, discussion prompts, and self-assessments are integrated within assessments to link fluent reading and comprehension.

*Adapted from Kuhn, M. R., Schwanenflugel, P. J., Meisinger, E. B. (2010). "Aligning Theory and Assessment of Reading Fluency: Automaticy, Prosody, and Definitions of Fluency." *Reading Research Quarterly*, 45 (2), 230–251.

Research About Fluency Assessment & Instruction*	How *Informal Assessments for Fluency Development* Supports Best Practices
Fluency likely has a reciprocal relationship with comprehension, both contributing to and possibly resulting from readers' understanding of text (Klauda & Guthrie, 2008; Stecker, Roser, & Martinez, 1998).	Rubrics, retellings, comprehension questions, and discussions are used to assess the connection between fluency and comprehension.
It is essential that fluency be seen as more than simply correct words per minute. Without the addition of some measure of prosody, there continues to be too high a risk that oral reading fluency will be seen only as a measure of quickly decoding a passage (Samuels, 2007) and that instruction will continue to follow suit (Wixson & Lipson, 2009). Prosodic measures such as the NAEP oral reading fluency scale (Pinnell, et. al, 1995) or the multidimensional fluency score guide (Rasinski, et. al 2009; Zutell & Rasinski, 1991) can serve as a rough gauge of how well students are integrating the suprasegmental features of language into their oral reading.	Fluency Scales, Self-Assessments, and Reading Conferences provide additional measures of fluency development in addition to leveled passages for identifying words per minute.
It remains critical that students are not focusing on rate at the expense of meaning; to prevent overemphasizing rapid decoding, a measure of comprehension should be used in conjunction with any evaluation of reading (Samuels, 2006). This can be undertaken in several ways, from brief discussions of the passage being read; to answering a range of questions from factual to inferential, which are related to the material; to student retellings of the text (McKenna & Stahl, 2003). It is important to evaluate students' oral reading (Daane et. al, 2005, McKenna & Stahl, 2003), because this is only one piece of information in a reader's profile.	Discussions, comprehension questions, and retellings are included to assess comprehension and fluency development.

*Adapted from Kuhn, M. R., Schwanenflugel, P. J., Meisinger, E. B. (2010). "Aligning Theory and Assessment of Reading Fluency: Automaticy, Prosody, and Definitions of Fluency." *Reading Research Quarterly*, 45 (2), 230–251.

Fluency Assessment Tools

Reading fluency, phrasing, and rate may be assessed any time a student reads aloud. A common means of measuring how well a student's oral reading corresponds to natural oral language is through the use of fluency rubrics and scales. A variety of assessment tools are included in this handbook to assess the elements of fluent reading.

Elements of Fluency to Assess	Fluency Assessment Tools	Frequency of Administering
Integration of Accuracy, Rate, and Prosody Oral Reading Fluency Decoding, Blending, Word Recognition Words per Minute (wpm) Rate Phrasing Comprehension	Fluency Rubrics (page 27) One-Minute Leveled Passages D-X (page 35) High-Frequency Word Phrase lists (pages 28 to 29)	Beginning/Middle/End of Year
Metacognitive Awareness Speed/Pacing, Pausing, Inflection/Intonation, Phrasing, Expression, Integration	Self-Assessments (pages 36 to 97)	Monthly
Oral Reading Performance Overall Public Speaking Performance/Delivery Reader's Theater performance	Reader's Theater Fluency Rubrics (pages 102 to 103) Reader's Theater Self-Assessments (pages 104 to 107) Reader's Theater Performance Assessments (page 108) Presentation Rubric (pages 109 to 110)	After a Reader's Theater or Oral Presentation

After administering, scoring, and analyzing assessment results, link assessments to instruction and choose mini-lessons to support fluency development. These mini-lessons can be taught in whole group, small group, or individually during reading conferences.

Mini-Lessons for Fluency Development

Element of Fluency	Skills	Mini-Lessons to Support
Rate	Speed/Pacing	Fast Slow Varied
	Pausing	Short Pause Full Stop Text Structure and Organization
Prosody	Inflection/Intonation	Pitch Volume Stress
	Phrasing	High-Frequency Word Phrases Subject/Predicate Phrases Dependent Clauses Prepositional Phrases Compound Sentences Units of Meaning in Complex Sentences
	Expression	Anticipation/Mood Characterization/Feelings Dramatic Expression

Reading Conferences

Individual Reading Conferences provide teachers with an opportunity to hear students read aloud from a self-selected title, or familiar reading of a text from small-group Guided Reading lessons. When observing students as they read aloud, conduct an oral reading and record anecdotal notes regarding how fluently students are reading. The Reading Conference recording form provides a template for key elements to include in your reading conferences.

Use the Fluency Rubric found on page 27 to note accuracy, rate, and expression. After listening to students read aloud orally, you may choose to provide additional support through mini-lessons, prompts (see also pages 18 to 23), or discussions related to linking fluent reading and overall comprehension of the text.

Individual Reading Conference

Name: _____ Date: _____

Book Title: _____ Author: _____ Pages: ___ to ___

Part One: Independent Reading Recap

Why did you choose this book? What are you interested in reading about? Do you need help finding a new book?

How is the difficulty of the text for you? How do you know?

Summarize or retell what has been happening (or what you have learned) so far.

Tell me what you remember most about what you've read.

Notes: _____

_____

_____

_____

_____

_____

_____

_____

_____

Part Two: Fluency Strategy Connections

How have you used the fluency strategies we've been learning about as a reader?

How have they helped you understand what you are reading? Explain.

How do you vary speed, pacing, phrasing, expression, intonation when you are reading? When do you adjust your reading? How do you know to adjust your rate or expression? How does that help you understand, or comprehend the text more?

Notes: _____

_____

_____

_____

_____

_____

_____

_____

Part Three: Oral Reading Record

Conduct an oral reading record on the independent reading selection or from a text read previously in small group Guided Reading lessons.

Attach the oral reading record form to your Individual Reading Conference note-taking form when finished.

Record notes for observations and next steps instructionally below.

Notes: _____

_____

_____

_____

_____

_____

_____

_____

Part Four: Action Planning

What are your strengths/needs/goals as a reader? How can I help you achieve them?

When do you anticipate finishing this book?

What is next on your list of must-read titles?

Notes: _____

_____

_____

_____

_____

_____

_____

_____

Prompting to Support Fluency Development

As an observant and responsive teacher, having a variety of prompting stems for a variety of purposes is a valuable resource. Each type of prompt has a distinct purpose for supporting learning and increasing proficiency with the elements of fluency.

Prompting Type	Purpose
Goal Oriented	Prompts for the reader who is not using the targeted strategy or skill at all. They offer a model or a benchmark of how the strategy or skill is used in reading.
Corrective Feedback/ Directive	Prompts for students who are beginning to use the strategy or skill but still need direct teaching or coaching on how to use it properly.
Self Monitoring/ Reflective	Prompts for students who have previously exhibited use of the strategy or skill in reading but are not consistent. These prompts remind students to be more reflective and think about the importance of using the strategy or skill at the right time.
Validating/Confirming	Prompts that are used at any time to validate or confirm a student's reading strategies and skills.

The following pages contain prompting stems to support the various elements of fluent reading with an emphasis on developing prosody. Use the prompts during guided practice or during independent reading. Remember to continually ask students to reflect on how they read a text affects their comprehension. This will promote awareness of the link between fluency and comprehension and aid in encouraging students to reflect and monitor reading to maintain understanding at all times.

Speed/Pacing Prompts

Goal Oriented
- Listen to me read. Can you read it like I do?
- Listen to how I read this. I am going to read this faster.
- Listen to how I read this. I am going to read this slower.
- Listen to my voice as I read the next sentence. Am I reading at a fluent pace?

Directive and Corrective Feedback
- Read these words faster.
- Read these words slower.
- Try that again and read slower.
- Try that again and read faster.
- Try moving your eyes quicker so you can read more words together.
- Read the text again and make it sound like you are talking.

Self-Monitoring and Reflection
- How did you pace your reading?
- Did you read that too fast or too slow?
- What did you do to read that faster/slower?
- How did you vary your pace in that passage?
- What did you notice about your reading?
- What made you read slower or faster?
- Where did you read too fast/slow?
- Where did you read at the right pace?

Validating and Confirming
- I liked the way you read it faster that time.
- I liked the way you slowed your reading down that time.
- Good job at varying your pace in the passage.
- You read at an appropriate rate. Great job!

Pausing Prompts

Goal Oriented

- Listen to me read this. Can you hear me take a little breath at the comma (semicolon, dash, colon, ellipsis)?
- The period (question mark, exclamation point) means your voice makes a full stop.
- When I make a short pause, I don't stop completely and break the flow of my reading.
- When I finish a sentence, I make a full stop before continuing with my reading.
- Notice what I do when I see a(n) comma (semicolon, dash, colon, ellipsis). My reading pauses briefly and then continues to help make ideas clear as I read.
- Notice what I do when I see a(n) period (question mark, exclamation point). My reading pauses with a full stop to show that I've read a complete sentence or idea.

Directive and Corrective Feedback

- Make a full stop at the period (question mark, exclamation point).
- Take a little breath when you see a(n) comma (semicolon, dash, colon, ellipsis).
- Read the punctuation.
- Read it like this with a short pause between the words.
- Read it like this with a full stop after the word.
- Make your pause longer.
- Make your pause shorter.

Self-Monitoring and Reflection

- How did you know to make a short pause here?
- How did you know to make a full stop here?
- Did you have any trouble knowing where to make a short pause or full stop as you read?
- Was your pausing too short, too long, or just right?
- Where did you make short pauses as you read?
- Where did you make full stops as you read?

Validating and Confirming

- Good—you took a little breath.
- Good—you made a full stop.
- I like the way you made a short pause/full stop here.
- I like the way you used the _____ punctuation mark to help you make a short pause/full stop here.
- Good—you used punctuation marks to help you know when to pause and for how long!

Inflection/Intonation Prompts

Goal Oriented

- Listen to how I read this. Can you hear my voice go down at the period?
- Listen to how I read this. Can you hear my voice go up at the question mark?
- Listen to how my voice gets louder.
- Listen to how my voice gets softer.
- Emphasize the word _____ like this.
- Notice what I do when I read the bold print (italicized words, words in all uppercase letters).

Directive and Corrective Feedback

- Make your voice go down at the period.
- Make your voice go up at the question mark.
- Read it louder.
- Read it softer.
- Stress the word _____ in this sentence.
- Watch for bold print (italicized words, words in all uppercase letters). Emphasize those words.

Self-Monitoring and Reflection

- What should your voice do when you see a period?
- What should your voice do when you see a question mark?
- Should your voice go up or down at this exclamation point?
- How did you know to read louder?
- How did you know to read softer?
- What made you emphasize the word _____?

Validating and Confirming

- Good job at making your voice rise and fall.
- You read that part louder/softer—way to think like the author!
- You stressed exactly the right words in that sentence. Good thinking!

Phrasing Prompts

Goal Oriented
- Listen to how reading sounds like talking.
- Listen to me read this part.
- Listen to how I group words together into phrases.
- Read it like this: _____.
- These words make sense together. Listen to how I read the words.
- Watch how I read the words without using my finger.
- Phrasing is not choppy reading like this:
  Look . . . for . . . some . . . people.

Directive and Corrective Feedback
- Now read the text just like I did.
- Repeat after me and make your reading sound like mine.
- Read the words _____ together as a group.
- Put your words together so that it sounds like talking.
- Read this much all together. (Cover part of the text.)
- Try that again and put the words together.
- Try reading with your eyes and not your finger.

Self-Monitoring and Reflection
- How did you make your reading sound like talking?
- What did you notice that made you group your words together?
- How did you know to put the words _____ together?
- How did grouping the words _____ together help you understand what you read?
- I noticed you stopped pointing with your finger. Did your eyes have any trouble keeping their place?
- Was your reading smooth or choppy?

Validating and Confirming
- I noticed that you put the words _____ together as a group. That makes your reading sound like talking.
- You put your words together. Good reading.
- You made your reading sound like talking.

Expression Prompts

Goal Oriented

- Let's read the title and look at the pictures. That will help us anticipate the mood of the passage.
- I see quotation marks, so the character is talking. I need to make my voice sound like the character's voice.
- I'll pretend to be that character. Listen to how I make my reading sound like he/she might talk.
- I need to make my voice, face, and body match what the author/character is saying when I read.
- Listen to me read this. Can you hear how excited (sad, proud, frightened) my voice sounds?

Directive and Corrective Feedback

- What kind of passage do you think this will be? How should you read it?
- Make your voice sound excited (sad, proud, frightened).
- Make your tone of voice match the author's/character's words.
- Make the character's voice match his/her actions and feelings.
- Read it like the author would say it.
- Repeat after me and read with expression.
- Use the punctuation to help you put expression in your voice when you read.

Self-Monitoring and Reflection

- How did you know what tone of voice to use?
- Did you read with expression?
- Where did you read with good expression?
- What part do you need to read again with more expression?
- Did you have any trouble reading with expression?
- Did you use pacing (pausing, inflection/ intonation, phrasing) to help you read with expression?

Validating and Confirming

- You noticed the funny pictures, so you used a happy tone of voice. Good thinking.
- You sounded excited (sad, proud, frightened) when you read that.
- I like the way you read it like the character was talking.
- I like the way you read with expression.
- I noticed that you read it just like talking.
- You paid careful attention to pacing (pausing, inflection/intonation, phrasing) to help you read with expression. Good work!

Assessment Walls

"The assessment wall makes the data visible, thus serving two important purposes: to study learning trends in student groups and to study reading progression for all students in relation to proficiency standards."

—Dorn and Soffos, 2001

Assessment walls (or folders) are used for identifying developmental progress (and strengths) as well as pinpointing instructional needs. Data can be displayed on a dedicated wall for faculty or grade-level data meetings, or in file folders for classroom use. Assessment walls can be used flexibly to examine student growth as a class or small group or for individual learners.

When reviewing data at data team meetings or individually, consider the following questions as you reflect on student learning and the next steps for instructional decisions.

How have the students progressed? What are their strengths? Needs?

What instructional methods or interventions are supporting learning, or not?

What are your goals for instruction, next steps for planning and supporting learning?

Data team meetings and the use of assessment walls that focus on fluency development provide opportunities to identify observable behaviors that link decoding, word recognition, vocabulary, and comprehension. Milestones included in the reference chart on page 25 as well as scores from using the Fluency Rubric on page 27 provide discussion topics to consider when reviewing assessment data and reflecting on student learning and progress.

Fluency Development Over Time

Developmental Reading Stages	Observable Reading Behaviors
Emergent	Fluently reads some high-frequency words (15–20) Decoding consonants and short vowels Beginning to attend to ending punctuation Beginning to read with expression and intonation
Early	Fluently reads many high-frequency words (100–150) Decoding blends, digraphs, dipthongs Uses ending punctuation, quotation marks Developing expression and intonation when reading
Transitional	Fluently reads a large number of high-frequency words (150–350+) Beginning to decode multisyllabic words Attends to punctuation for phrasing Uses understandings of grammatical structures to adjust fluency when reading Integrates word recognition, decoding, and expression more consistently when reading
Advanced	Utilizes an expanding bank of high-frequency words (350+) Decodes multisyllabic words consistently Uses word-solving strategies to maintain comprehension and fluent reading of text Uses text structure and genre features to adjust fluency when reading Consistently integrates accuracy, rate, and prosody when reading

Fluency Rubrics

Fluency Rubrics are used to identify how students are integrating all aspects of fluency (accuracy, rate, prosody) as they read aloud. Other assessment tools such as the NAEP Oral Reading Fluency Scale (Pinnell, et. al, 1995) and the fluency scoring guide (Rasinski & Zutell, 1991) are additional tools to reference when assessing oral reading fluency. Use the following Fluency Rubric to note accuracy, rate, prosody, and how students are integrating together for comprehension and fluent reading. As you conduct informal reading conferences or any time you listen to students read aloud from an independent or instructional level text, you can use the rubric for consistently evaluating their fluency progress.

Fluency Rubric

Student: _____ Date: _____

The key elements of reading fluency — accuracy, speed, pacing, pausing, inflection/intonation, expression, phrasing, and the integration of these skills — may be assessed any time a student reads aloud. Discuss the assessment rubric, modeling each description, so students know what you expect.

Rating Scale	Elements of Fluent Reading
	Accuracy
1	Multiple attempts at decoding words without success. Word reading accuracy is inadequate/poor (below 90%).
2	Attempts to self correct errors, usually unsuccessful. Word reading accuracy is marginal (between 90%–93%).
3	Attempts to self correct errors are successful. Word reading accuracy is good (between 94%–97%).
4	Most words are read correctly on initial attempt. Minimal self-corrections, all successful. Word reading accuracy is excellent (98%–100%).
	Rate: Speed, Pacing, Pausing
1	Slow and laborious reading.
2	Reading is either moderately slow or inappropriately fast, pausing is infrequent or ignored.
3	Unbalanced combination of slow and fast reading containing inconsistent pausing.
4	Reading is consistently natural, conversational, and appropriately varied (resembling natural oral language).
	Prosody: Inflection/Intonation and Expression
1	Reads in an inexpressive, monotone manner and does not attend to punctuation.
2	Reads with some intonation (pitch/tone/volume/stress) and some attention to punctuation. Reads in a monotone at times.
3	Reads by adjusting intonation (pitch/tone/volume/stress) inappropriately. Consistently attends to punctuation.
4	Reads with intonation that reflects feeling, anticipation, tension, character development, and mood.
	Prosody: Phrasing
1	Reads word by word. Does not attend to author's syntax or sentence structures. Has limited sense of phrase boundaries.
2	Reads slowly and in a choppy manner, usually in two-word phrases. Some attention is given to author's syntax and sentence structures.
3	Reads in phrases of three to four words. Appropriate syntax is used.
4	Reads in longer, more meaningful phrases. Regularly uses phrase boundaries, punctuation, sentence structure, and author's syntax to reflect comprehension and fluent reading.
	Integration
1	Reading is monotone, laborious, inexpressive, and accuracy rate is poor (below 90%).
2	Reading is unbalanced with inconsistent rate and pacing, some phrasing, inadequate intonation & expression, marginal accuracy (between 90%–93%).
3	Reading is somewhat adjusted with some variation in rate, appropriate prosody, and with good accuracy (between 94%–97%).
4	Reads in an integrated manner with high accuracy, rate, intonation, and expression on a consistent basis. Fluent reading reflects understanding and interpretation of text.

High Frequency Word Phrases

The following leveled phrase lists are short phrases made from high-frequency words. These lists are designed for repeated practice of high-frequency words in a short context, as opposed to reading isolated word lists.

Research has shown that repeated practice of reading high-frequency words can have a beneficial effect on students' word-recognition skills. These activities require that students practice reading the words until they can read them automatically without effort. Teachers may want to write these phrases on cards and have students practice the phrase lists at their designated reading level, to aid with phrasing, accuracy, and word recognition.

Level D
We made it.
I want it.
Go to sleep.
Run fast.
Can you see?
I can help.
This is my home.
I am big.
I can ride.
He has it.

Level E
No way!
He ran away!
This is not it.
I cannot come.
How many?
What did you do?
There she is!
Did you eat it all?
I made it.
I saw Dad.

Level F
I like him.
Sit down.
Can you come?
I can't go.
We have a dog.
Go get her.
He said to go.
I'll go with Mom.
See the cat.
Did you see her?

Level G
Could you go?
We like to go.
We like to write.
He said to come.
Can you write your name?
I don't care.
It is morning.
You are late.
Where did you go?
Where is Mom?

Level H
What is your number?
Look behind you.
Which one is yours?
Look at the water.
The dog is big.
Can you see in?
Come and see my room.
Have you been here?
How do you know?
It is a long way.

Level I
Are you there?
It is as big as you.
Will you go first?
He will be good.
Will you come to my house?
It is at my house.
How did you get it?
Which bus will you take?
What is the first word?
What is your name?

Level J

Where are you?
I need you.
What is your part?
How many people are there?
Which one would you like?
Can you get from here to there?
Which one do you like?
Did you come the long way?
It is time to go.
How did you get here?

Level K

Come and take a look.
What is your last name?
Mother says to go now.
You are a good man.
What do you like to play?
Go over the river.
Will you give it back?
Do you know why?
Can you put it up there?
We want to go home.

Level L

How many are there?
I don't feel good.
Can you come over?
I will only take a little.
That is a good sentence.
Is that a new sound?
That is just the same.
How many years ago did
  you go there?
Look at my new place.
She is not mean.

Level M

Can you go after the game?
He is a little boy.
Do you want to go with her?
Where is your home?
You must be right.
This must be it.
You have such a big house.
They were here.
Do you have a picture?
Can you show me around?

Level N

Can you help me out?
We need more people.
Can you spell your name?
Get in two lines.
Are you telling the truth?
Can you write one sentence?
This must be it.
It's still here.
Can you play it again?
We found it over there.

Level O

Do you like to learn?
Try your best.
Can you stay awhile?
Next time we will go.
We will plant the trees.
That is a good thought.
Don't go near the car.
We started running.
I can run for miles.
We walked four miles.

Level P

We walked near the sea.
She lived a long life.
She is on the team.
That is almost enough.
That is a good idea.
He is a very important person.
Can you take the car?
Can you stop the music?
I need to talk to my father.
Look at the white clouds.

Level Q

Leave it to me.
This is an important idea.
My family watched the game.
I missed all of the people.
The plant began to grow.
That is almost enough.
Read your book to me.
This is a long list of people.
It is the first day of school.
It's time to eat.

Level R

What happened to you?
Do you remember me?
Do you have any questions?
Do you want a piece of pie?
I heard he made one hundred.
He cried and cried.
Did you complete all of
  the problems?
We went across the room?
Today, we are going north.
He fell upon the ground.

One-Minute Oral Reading Fluency Assessment

The One-Minute Oral Reading Fluency Assessment is used to evaluate students' reading rate and document their progress over time in comparison to national fluency norms. This assessment can be used to gather information on students' oral fluency and phrasing. The assessment determines the number of words the student reads correctly per minute and also provides a rubric for assessing phrasing, pitch, stress, intonation, and comprehension. It is recommended that teachers formally assess students' reading fluency at the beginning, in the middle and end of the school year. This information can become part of students' permanent portfolio for documentation and accountability. Students may be assessed individually when most convenient for teachers—at the beginning or end of the day, or when appropriate during a portion of small-group reading time, or when students are engaged in independent reading.

Preparing to Administer One-Minute Oral Reading Fluency Assessments

Prior to administering the one-minute assessments, copy the leveled passages and teacher recording forms for each level (pages 34 to 97). Then create a folder for each student. Throughout the year, store the students' assessments in these folders, or place the assessments in individual student portfolios.

Instructions

Reading fluency, phrasing, and rate may be assessed whenever a student reads aloud. Use the procedure below to measure oral reading fluency.

1. Select the fluency assessment passage at the student's independent reading level (95–100% accuracy). You will also need a copy of the reproducible record form for this level.
2. Give the student a brief introduction to the passage. Ask the student to read the passage using his or her best voice.
3. As the student reads, mark any errors with a slash mark through the words. Use the assessment guidelines below.
4. At the end of one minute, mark the point in the text where the student was reading by circling the last word read. Allow the student to finish reading the passage.
5. Ask the student the comprehension questions on the back of the card.
6. Count up the number of words read correctly. Record this information on the record form. Use the chart in Figure 1 to compare the student's performance to the national norm for the grade level and time of year. Document this on the record form.
7. Use the Oral Fluency and Phrasing Rating Rubric to rate the student's fluency and phrasing while reading (page 33).

Scoring Guidelines

Words read correctly include words that are self-corrected within three seconds of an error. (Mark each self-correction with **SC** above the word.) Correctly read words that are repeated are not counted as errors.

Words read incorrectly should be marked with a /. The following errors are counted as incorrect:

- Mispronounced words—words that are misread.
- Word substitutions—one word read for another word. For example, **boat** for **ship**.
- Omissions or skipped words—words that are not read.
- Hesitations—If the student hesitates for three seconds or longer, say the word and have the student continue reading.

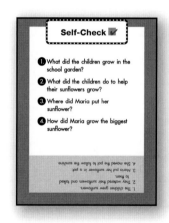

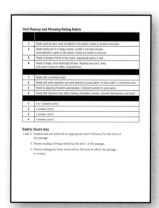

Using Assessment Results to Inform Instruction

Analyze assessment results to identify student strengths, needs, and next steps for instruction. Consider the following questions as you review and reflect on student performance.

What does the oral reading fluency rubric show you about how a student is progressing as a reader? What areas are in need of additional support?

What connection between fluency and comprehension is evident?

How will results inform small group instruction and individual reading conferences?

One-Minute Timed Reading Rate Goals

Text Level	Grade Level	Reading Rate Goal (Words Per Minute)
D	First (beginning of year)	20
E		25
F		30
G		40
H		50
I	First (end of year)	60
J	Second (beginning of year)	65
K		75
L		85
M	Second (end of year)	95
N	Third (beginning of year)	95
O		105
P	Third (end of year)	115
Q	Fourth (beginning of year)	115
R	Fourth (end of year)	120
S	Fifth (beginning of year)	120
T		125
U	Fifth (end of year)	130
V	Sixth (beginning of year)	135
W		140
X	Sixth (end of year)	145
Y	Seventh (beginning of year)	145
Z	Seventh (end of year)	150

Adapted from Hasbrouck & Tindall (2006).

Oral Fluency and Phrasing Rating Rubric

Rating Scale	Phrasing and Fluency
1	Reads word by word. Does not attend to the author's syntax or sentence structures.
2	Reads slowly and in a choppy manner, usually in two-word phrases. Some attention is given to the author's syntax and sentence structures.
3	Reads in phrases of three or four words. Appropriate syntax is used.
4	Reads in longer, more meaningful phrases. Regularly uses pitch, stress, and author's syntax to reflect comprehension.
	Intonation
1	Reads with a monotone voice.
2	Reads with some intonation and some attention to punctuation. At times reads in a monotone voice.
3	Reads by adjusting intonation appropriately. Consistently attends to punctuation.
4	Reads with intonation that reflects feeling, anticipation, tension, character development, and mood.
	Comprehension
1	0 or 1 answers correct
2	2 answers correct
3	3 answers correct
4	4 answers correct

Rubric Score Key

1 and 2: Student has not achieved an appropriate level of fluency for the level of the passage.

3: Fluent reading is being refined at the level of the passage.

4: Fluent reading has been achieved for the level at which the passage is written.

One-Minute Fluency Leveled Passages Assessments

Teacher Name: _____ Grade Level: _____

Student Name	Beginning of Year Text Level/WPM	Mid Year Text Level/WPM	End of Year Text Level/WPM

One-Minute Oral Reading Fluency Assessment Record Form • Level D-E

Name: _____ Date: _____

Correct Words per Minute: _____ National Norm of Words per Minute: _____

Playing Ball

Tim and Jim play ball. They _____ 6
run. They jump. They throw _____ 11
the ball. They kick the ball. _____ 17
They have fun. _____ 20

"Time for bed!" says Mom. _____ 25

"Can we play more?" asks Tim. _____ 31

"You need to sleep now," _____ 36
says Mom. _____ 38

Tim and Jim go to bed. Mom _____ 45
tells them a story. The story _____ 51
is about two boys. The boys _____ 57
play ball. They run. They jump. _____ 63
They throw the ball. They kick _____ 69

the ball. The boys have fun. _____ 75

Tim and Jim smile. Soon the _____ 81
boys are asleep. _____ 84

Oral Reading Fluency Rubric

	Rubric Score
Accuracy	1 2 3 4
Speed/Pacing	1 2 3 4
Pausing	1 2 3 4
Inflection/Intonation	1 2 3 4
Phrasing	1 2 3 4
Integration	1 2 3 4

Rubric Score Key
1 and 2: Student has not achieved an appropriate level of fluency for the level of the passage.

3: Fluent reading is being refined at the level of the passage.

4: Fluent reading has been achieved for the level at which the passage is written.

Playing Ball

Tim and Jim play ball. They _____ 6
run. They jump. They throw _____ 11
the ball. They kick the ball. _____ 17
They have fun. _____ 20

"Time for bed!" says Mom. _____ 25

"Can we play more?" asks Tim. _____ 31

"You need to sleep now," _____ 36
says Mom. _____ 38

Informal Assessments for Fluency Development

Tim and Jim go to bed. Mom _____ 45
tells them a story. The story _____ 51
is about two boys. The boys _____ 57
play ball. They run. They jump. _____ 63
They throw the ball. They kick _____ 69
the ball. The boys have fun. _____ 75

Tim and Jim smile. Soon the _____ 81
boys are asleep. _____ 84

Self-Check

1. **Tim and Jim kicked the _____.**
2. **Why did Tim and Jim go to bed?**
3. **Did Tim and Jim like Mom's story? How can you tell?**

1. Tim and Jim kicked the ball.
2. Mom said, "You need to sleep now."
3. Yes, Tim and Jim smiled.

One-Minute Oral Reading Fluency Assessment Record Form • Level F

Name: _____ Date: _____

Correct Words per Minute: _____ National Norm of Words per Minute: _____

Juan Likes to Run

Juan likes to run. Juan runs ——— 6
by himself. He runs with his ——— 12
dog. He runs with his dad. ——— 18
He runs with his friends. ——— 23

When does Juan run? Juan ——— 28
runs in the morning. He runs ——— 34
in the afternoon. He runs in ——— 40
the evening. ——— 42

"I like to see you run, Juan," ——— 49
Mom says. ——— 51

"I *like* to run," Juan says, ——— 57
running around Mom. ——— 60

"Do you know what time ——— 65
it is?" Mom asks. ——— 69

Juan looks at the clock. He ——— 75
takes small, slow steps. His ——— 80
mother smiles. Juan stops ——— 84
running. It is time for bed! ——— 90

Oral Reading Fluency Rubric

	Rubric Score			
Accuracy	1	2	3	4
Speed/Pacing	1	2	3	4
Pausing	1	2	3	4
Inflection/Intonation	1	2	3	4
Phrasing	1	2	3	4
Integration	1	2	3	4

Rubric Score Key

1 and 2: Student has not achieved an appropriate level of fluency for the level of the passage.

3: Fluent reading is being refined at the level of the passage.

4: Fluent reading has been achieved for the level at which the passage is written.

Informal Assessments for Fluency Development

Juan Likes to Run

Juan likes to run. Juan runs ___ 6
by himself. He runs with his ___ 12
dog. He runs with his dad. ___ 18
He runs with his friends. ___ 23

When does Juan run? Juan ___ 28
runs in the morning. He runs ___ 34
in the afternoon. He runs in ___ 40
the evening. ___ 42

"I like to see you run, Juan," ___ 49
Mom says. ___ 51

"I *like* to run," Juan says, running around Mom.

———— 57

———— 60

"Do you know what time it is?" Mom asks.

———— 65

———— 69

Juan looks at the clock. He takes small, slow steps. His mother smiles. Juan stops running. It is time for bed!

———— 75

———— 80

———— 84

———— 90

Self-Check

1. What does Juan like to do?

2. Why did Juan stop running?

3. What will Juan do when he gets up? How do you know?

1. Juan likes to run.
2. Juan looked at the clock. It was time for bed.
3. Juan will run. He runs in the morning. He runs every place he goes.

One-Minute Oral Reading Fluency Assessment Record Form • Level F

Name: _____ Date: _____

Correct Words per Minute: _____ National Norm of Words per Minute: _____

The Walking Bus

Ten children at Park Lane School go	7
home in the walking bus.	12
Mrs. Green walks in front of	18
the bus. Mr. Scott walks in back of	26
the bus. The children walk in the	33
middle.	34
"Here we go!" says Mrs. Green.	40
"Look out for cars."	44
The bus walks slowly. It stops	50
at Ben's house. It stops	55
at Maria's house. It stops and	61
stops until all ten children	66
are home!	68

Oral Reading Fluency Rubric

	Rubric Score	Comments:
Phrasing and Fluency	1 2 3 4	
Intonation		
Comprehension		

Rubric Score Key

1 and 2: Student has not achieved an appropriate level of fluency for the level of the passage.

3: Fluent reading is being refined at the level of the passage.

4: Fluent reading has been achieved for the level at which the passage is written.

The Walking Bus

Ten children at Park Lane School go   7
home in the walking bus.   12
Mrs. Green walks in front of   18
the bus. Mr. Scott walks in back of   26
the bus. The children walk in the   33
middle.   34

"Here we go!" says Mrs. Green.   40
"Look out for cars."   44

The bus walks slowly. It stops   50
at Ben's house. It stops   55
at Maria's house. It stops and stops   62
until all ten children   66
are home!   68

Self-Check

1. What does a walking bus do?

2. Who walked in front of the walking bus?

3. How many children took the walking bus home?

4. Where did the walking bus stop?

1. A walking bus takes children home from school.

2. Mrs. Green walked in front of the walking bus.

3. Ten children took the walking bus home.

4. The walking bus stopped at all the children's houses.

Name: _____   Date: _____

Correct Words per Minute: _____   National Norm of Words per Minute: _____

The Biggest Sunflower

Children at Sunset School were	5
growing sunflowers in the garden.	10
They watered their sunflowers to	15
help them grow. They talked to	21
their sunflowers to help them	26
grow.	27
But Maria put her sunflower in	33
a pot. All day long she moved	40
the pot to follow the sunshine.	46
Her sunflower grew very big.	51
It became the biggest sunflower.	56
"My sunflower likes sunshine," said	61
Maria. "So where the Sun goes,	67
my sunflower goes, too!"	71

Oral Reading Fluency Rubric

	Rubric Score	Comments:
Phrasing and Fluency	1 2 3 4	
Intonation		
Comprehension		

Rubric Score Key
1 and 2: Student has not achieved an appropriate level of fluency for the level of the passage.

3: Fluent reading is being refined at the level of the passage.

4: Fluent reading has been achieved for the level at which the passage is written.

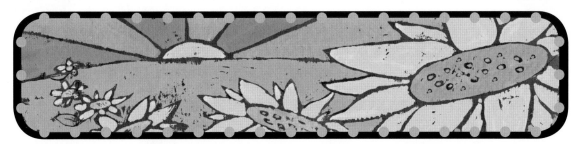

The Biggest Sunflower

Children at Sunset School were   5
growing sunflowers in the garden.   10
They watered their sunflowers to   15
help them grow. They talked to   21
their sunflowers to help them   26
grow.   27

But Maria put her sunflower in   33
a pot. All day long she moved the   40
pot to follow the sunshine.   46
Her sunflower grew very big.   51
It became the biggest sunflower.   56

"My sunflower likes sunshine," said   61
Maria. "So where the Sun goes, my   67
sunflower goes, too!"   71

Self-Check

1. What did the children grow in the school garden?

2. What did the children do to help their sunflowers grow?

3. Where did Maria put her sunflower?

4. How did Maria grow the biggest sunflower?

1. The children grew sunflowers.
2. They watered their sunflowers and talked to them.
3. Maria put her sunflower in a pot.
4. She moved the pot to follow the sunshine.

Name: _____   Date: _____

Correct Words per Minute: _____   National Norm of Words per Minute: _____

The Scruffy Dog

It was bath day for Mr. Green's dog.   8
"Come here, Scruffy," said Mr. Green.   14
"It's time for your bath."   19

Scruffy didn't like to be washed with dog   27
soap. He didn't like to be brushed with   35
a dog comb. He liked to be scruffy and   44
dirty.   45

"Here I come, Scruffy," said Mr. Green.   52
"You can't run away from me this time."   60

Scruffy ran into the yard and hid   67
from Mr. Green. But Mr. Green found   74
him, and now Scruffy is fluffy!   80

Oral Reading Fluency Rubric

	Rubric Score	Comments:
Phrasing and Fluency	1 2 3 4	
Intonation		
Comprehension		

Rubric Score Key
1 and 2: Student has not achieved an appropriate level of
fluency for the level of the passage.
3: Fluent reading is being refined at the level of
the passage.
4: Fluent reading has been achieved for the level at
which the passage is written.

The Scruffy Dog

It was bath day for Mr. Green's dog.   8
"Come here, Scruffy," said Mr. Green.   14
"It's time for your bath."   19

Scruffy didn't like to be washed with dog   27
soap. He didn't like to be brushed with   35
a dog comb. He liked to be scruffy and   44
dirty.   45

"Here I come, Scruffy," said Mr. Green.   52
"You can't run away from me this time."   60

Scruffy ran into the yard and hid   67
from Mr. Green. But Mr. Green found   74
him, and now Scruffy is fluffy!   80

Self-Check

1. What day was it for Mr. Green's dog?

2. Why did Scruffy run away?

3. Where did Scruffy hide?

4. What did Mr. Green do when he found Scruffy?

1. It was bath day.
2. Scruffy didn't like baths.
3. He hid in the yard.
4. He gave Scruffy a bath.

Name: _____ Date: _____

Correct Words per Minute: _____ National Norm of Words per Minute: _____

The Sleepy Dog

Sara had a cat, but she always wanted   8
to have a dog. "Jump, Snowy, jump,"   15
Sara said to her cat. The cat just   23
went to sleep. "Sit, Snowy, sit," Sara said   31
to her cat. The cat just went to sleep.   40

Then Sara went with her mom to look   48
after her grandpa's dog. "Run after   54
the ball, Jack," Sara said to the dog.   62
He shut his eyes and went to sleep.   70

"Jack would make a very good cat!"   77
said Sara as she laughed.   82

Oral Reading Fluency Rubric

	Rubric Score	Comments:
Phrasing and Fluency	1 2 3 4	
Intonation		
Comprehension		

Rubric Score Key

1 and 2: Student has not achieved an appropriate level of fluency for the level of the passage.

3: Fluent reading is being refined at the level of the passage.

4: Fluent reading has been achieved for the level at which the passage is written.

The Sleepy Dog

Sara had a cat, but she always wanted   8
to have a dog. "Jump, Snowy, jump," Sara   15
said to her cat. The cat just   23
went to sleep. "Sit, Snowy, sit," Sara said to   31
her cat. The cat just went to sleep.   40

Then Sara went with her mom to look after   48
her grandpa's dog. "Run after   54
the ball, Jack," Sara said to the dog.   62

He shut his eyes and went to sleep.   70

"Jack would make a very good cat!" said   77
Sara as she laughed.   83

Self-Check ✔

1. What kind of pet did Sara want?
2. Where did Sara go with her mom?
3. What did Sara's cat always do?
4. How was Grandpa's dog like Sara's cat?

1. Sara wanted a dog.
2. Sara and her mom went to take care of Sara's grandpa's dog.
3. Sara's cat always went to sleep.
4. Both the dog and the cat liked to go to sleep.

Name: _____ Date: _____

Correct Words per Minute: _____ National Norm of Words per Minute: _____

The Happy Robot

Robot sat down at the kitchen table.   7

"Would you like something to eat?"   13
asked Robot's owner.   16

"No, I'm not hungry," said Robot. But   23
then it ate 10 banana-nut muffins. "I   29
want to look at some of your wires,"   37
said Robot's owner. She gently opened   43
the door to Robot's tummy and looked   50
inside.   51

"Your wires are messed up, so you eat   59
when you're not hungry."   63
When Robot was fixed, it smiled and   70
said, "Thank you for fixing me. Now I   78
will not feel so stuffed."   83

Oral Reading Fluency Rubric

	Rubric Score	Comments:
Phrasing and Fluency	1 2 3 4	
Intonation		
Comprehension		

Rubric Score Key

1 and 2: Student has not achieved an appropriate level of fluency for the level of the passage.

3: Fluent reading is being refined at the level of the passage.

4: Fluent reading has been achieved for the level at which the passage is written.

The Happy Robot

Robot sat down at the kitchen table. 7

"Would you like something to eat?" asked 13
Robot's owner. 16

"No, I'm not hungry," said Robot. But then it 23
ate 10 banana-nut muffins. "I 29
want to look at some of your wires," 37
said Robot's owner. She gently opened 43
the door to Robot's tummy and looked 50
inside. 51

"Your wires are messed up, so you eat 59
when you're not hungry." 63

When Robot was fixed, it smiled and said, 70
"Thank you for fixing me. Now I will not feel 78
so stuffed." 83

Self-Check

1. What did Robot eat?

2. If Robot was not hungry, why did it eat?

3. Who fixed Robot?

4. Why was Robot happy to be fixed?

1. Robot ate 10 banana-nut muffins.
2. It ate because its wires were messed up.
3. Robot's owner fixed it.
4. He wouldn't feel stuffed anymore.

Name: _____ Date: _____

Correct Words per Minute: _____ National Norm of Words per Minute: _____

The Weather Watcher

The weather watcher watched the weather — 6
every day. He told people watching TV — 13
when it was going to be sunny, windy, — 21
rainy, or snowy. — 24

One day the weather watcher got tired — 31
of watching the weather. He decided he — 38
wanted to watch other things. So he — 45
went on vacation. — 48

He watched strong winds blow sailboats — 54
over in the sea. He watched heavy rain — 62
flood streets and sidewalks. Wherever he — 68
went, the weather caused problems. So — 74
he returned to watch the weather in — 81
order to warn people when bad weather — 88
was coming. — 90

Oral Reading Fluency Rubric

	Rubric Score				Comments:
Phrasing and Fluency	1	2	3	4	
Intonation					
Comprehension					

Rubric Score Key

1 and 2: Student has not achieved an appropriate level of fluency for the level of the passage.

3: Fluent reading is being refined at the level of the passage.

4: Fluent reading has been achieved for the level at which the passage is written.

The Weather Watcher

The weather watcher watched the weather 6
every day. He told people watching TV 13
when it was going to be sunny, windy, 21
rainy, or snowy. 24

One day the weather watcher got tired 31
of watching the weather. He decided he 38
wanted to watch other things. So he went 45
on vacation. 48

He watched strong winds blow sailboats 54
over in the sea. He watched heavy rain 62
flood streets and sidewalks. Wherever he 68
went, the weather caused problems. So 74
he returned to watch the weather in 81
order to warn people when bad weather 88
was coming. 90

Self-Check ✔

1. What did the weather watcher do?
2. Why did the weather watcher stop watching the weather?
3. What did the weather watcher see when he went on vacation?
4. Why did the weather watcher go back to watching the weather?

1. He watched and reported the weather.
2. He got tired of doing it.
3. He saw strong winds blowing over sailboats and rain flooding streets.
4. He wanted to warn people when bad weather was coming.

Name: _____ Date: _____

Correct Words per Minute: _____ National Norm of Words per Minute: _____

The Red Pig

The baby pink pig looked at the other pigs.   9

"You all need a bath," she said. "I'm not   18
smelly, and I don't have mud all over me.   27
I'm lovely, clean, and pink."   32

The other pigs looked at the baby pig. Then   41
they looked up at the hot sun and smiled.   50
Soon the baby pig got hotter and hotter. She   59
also got pinker and pinker. The pigs said,   67
"You're lovely and clean, but you're not pink.   75
Your skin is red."   79

So the baby red pig jumped into the brown   88
mud and was never, ever pink or red again!   97

Oral Reading Fluency Rubric

	Rubric Score	Comments:
Phrasing and Fluency	1 2 3 4	
Intonation		
Comprehension		

Rubric Score Key

1 and 2: Student has not achieved an appropriate level of fluency for the level of the passage.

3: Fluent reading is being refined at the level of the passage.

4: Fluent reading has been achieved for the level at which the passage is written.

THE RED PIG

The baby pink pig looked at the other pigs. 9

"You all need a bath," she said. "I'm not 18
smelly, and I don't have mud all over me. 27
I'm lovely, clean, and pink." 32

The other pigs looked at the baby pig. Then 41
they looked up at the hot sun and smiled. 50
Soon the baby pig got hotter and hotter. She 59
also got pinker and pinker. The pigs said, 67
"You're lovely and clean, but you're not pink. 75
Your skin is red." 79

So the baby red pig jumped into the brown 88
mud and was never, ever pink or red again! 97

Self-Check

1. Who is the main character in the story?

2. What is the setting of the story?

3. What did the baby pig notice about the other pigs?

4. What did the baby pig do when her skin got red?

1. The baby pig is the main character.
2. The setting is the barnyard.
3. The other pigs were all muddy and smelly.
4. She jumped into the mud.

Name: _____ Date: _____

Correct Words per Minute: _____ National Norm of Words per Minute: _____

Molly's Smile

Molly is 3 years old, and she doesn't talk very — 9
much. When she was 2, her family waited and — 17
waited for her to talk. But Molly just smiled — 26
and didn't say much. — 30

Molly's family took her to a children's doctor. — 38
The doctor thought Molly just learned things — 45
more slowly than other children. Molly didn't — 52
talk to the doctor, but she gave him a big — 62
smile. — 63

Her family took her to a speech teacher, who — 72
helped Molly learn how to say words. Slowly, — 80
Molly started to catch up with other children. — 88

Molly still likes smiling. Her smile speaks — 95
1,000 words! — 96

Oral Reading Fluency Rubric

	Rubric Score	Comments:
Phrasing and Fluency	1 2 3 4	
Intonation		
Comprehension		

Rubric Score Key

1 and 2: Student has not achieved an appropriate level of fluency for the level of the passage.

3: Fluent reading is being refined at the level of the passage.

4: Fluent reading has been achieved for the level at which the passage is written.

MOLLY'S SMILE

Molly is 3 years old, and she doesn't talk very much. When she was 2, her family waited and waited for her to talk. But Molly just smiled and didn't say much.

Molly's family took her to a children's doctor. The doctor thought Molly just learned things more slowly than other children. Molly didn't talk to the doctor, but she gave him a big smile.

Her family took her to a speech teacher, who helped Molly learn how to say words. Slowly, Molly started to catch up with other children.

Molly still likes smiling. Her smile speaks 1,000 words!

9
17
26
30

38
45
52
62
63

72
80
88

95
96

Self-Check

1. Who is the main character in the story?

2. What was the problem?

3. How was the problem solved?

4. What speaks 1,000 words?

1. The main character is Molly.

2. Molly was 3 years old and did not talk very much.

3. Molly's parents took her to a speech teacher.

4. Molly's smile speaks 1,000 words.

One-Minute Oral Reading Fluency Assessment Record Form • Level N

Name: _____ Date: _____

Correct Words per Minute: _____ National Norm of Words per Minute: _____

The Rainbow Mailbox

Lana and her mom wanted to make a colorful — 9
mailbox. — 10

"What kind of mailbox do you want to build?" — 19
asked Lana's mom. "How about a dinosaur mailbox?" — 27

"That's not very colorful," replied Lana. "Why — 34
don't we build a rainbow mailbox of red, orange, — 43
yellow, green, blue, indigo, and violet?" — 49

"Then I think we'd better go to the paint store," — 59
said Lana's mom, laughing. — 63

"Oops, we need eight colors. I forgot about gold — 72
paint for the pot of gold that's at the end of the — 84
rainbow!" said Lana. — 87

When the mail carrier saw the rainbow mailbox, — 95
she said to Lana, "Your mailbox makes me cheerful — 104
on rainy days!" — 107

Oral Reading Fluency Rubric

	Rubric Score	Comments:
Phrasing and Fluency	1 2 3 4	
Intonation		
Comprehension		

Rubric Score Key

1 and 2: Student has not achieved an appropriate level of fluency for the level of the passage.

3: Fluent reading is being refined at the level of the passage.

4: Fluent reading has been achieved for the level at which the passage is written.

Informal Assessments for Fluency Development

The Rainbow Mailbox

Lana and her mom wanted to make a colorful mailbox.

"What kind of mailbox do you want to build?" asked Lana's mom. "How about a dinosaur mailbox?"

"That's not very colorful," replied Lana. "Why don't we build a rainbow mailbox of red, orange, yellow, green, blue, indigo, and violet?"

"Then I think we'd better go to the paint store," said Lana's mom, laughing.

"Oops, we need eight colors. I forgot about gold paint for the pot of gold that's at the end of the rainbow!" said Lana.

When the mail carrier saw the rainbow mailbox, she said to Lana, "Your mailbox makes me cheerful on rainy days!"

9
10
19
27
34
43
49
59
63
72
84
87
95
104
107

Self-Check

1. Why didn't Lana want to build a dinosaur mailbox?

2. What did Lana and her mom almost forget at the paint store?

3. Why did they need the gold paint?

4. Why did the mail carrier like the rainbow mailbox?

1. She thought it was not colorful enough.
2. They almost forgot the gold paint.
3. They needed the gold paint to paint a pot of gold at the end of the rainbow.
4. It made her feel cheerful on rainy days.

Name: _____ Date: _____

Correct Words per Minute: _____ National Norm of Words per Minute: _____

Scarecrow Joe

The old crows weren't afraid of Scarecrow Joe.   8
Farmer Robin knew that she had to do something,   17
so she dressed Joe in black clothes.   24

"That will make you look scary," she said to   33
Scarecrow Joe.   35

But the crows thought that Joe looked like a big,   45
black, friendly bird. They just kept eating Farmer   53
Robin's corn.   55

One day an eagle flew over the field and saw the   66
crows eating Farmer Robin's corn. The eagle decided   74
to help poor, frightened Scarecrow Joe by swooping   82
down and scaring the crows.   87

The eagle said, "I'm an eagle who scares crows,"   96
and sat on Joe's shoulder. From that day on,   105
the eagle and the scarecrow kept Farmer Robin's   113
corn safe.   115

Oral Reading Fluency Rubric

	Rubric Score	Comments:
Phrasing and Fluency	1 2 3 4	
Intonation		
Comprehension		

Rubric Score Key

1 and 2: Student has not achieved an appropriate level of fluency for the level of the passage.

3: Fluent reading is being refined at the level of the passage.

4: Fluent reading has been achieved for the level at which the passage is written.

Scarecrow Joe

The old crows weren't afraid of Scarecrow Joe.   8
Farmer Robin knew that she had to do something,   17
so she dressed Joe in black clothes.   24

"That will make you look scary," she said to   33
Scarecrow Joe.   35

But the crows thought that Joe looked like a big,   45
black, friendly bird. They just kept eating Farmer   53
Robin's corn.   55

One day an eagle flew over the field and saw the   66
crows eating Farmer Robin's corn. The eagle decided   74
to help poor, frightened Scarecrow Joe by swooping   82
down and scaring the crows.   87

The eagle said, "I'm an eagle who scares crows,"   96
and sat on Joe's shoulder. From that day on,   105
the eagle and the scarecrow kept Farmer Robin's   113
corn safe.   115

Self-Check

1. What is the setting of the story?

2. What did Farmer Robin do to make Scarecrow Joe look scary?

3. Why weren't the crows scared by Scarecrow Joe?

4. How did the problem get solved?

Name: _____ Date: _____

Correct Words per Minute: _____ National Norm of Words per Minute: _____

The Cat Show

"I am going to enter Ebony in the big cat show,   11
but first I have to give her a bath," said Jessie.   22

Ebony sensed that she was about to get a bath   32
and scrambled up a tall cottonwood tree. Jessie   40
pleaded and pleaded for her to come down. But   49
Ebony just sat high up in the tree, ignoring Jessie's   59
pleas. All the neighbors came out and tried to help   69
Jessie get Ebony down.   73

Jessie didn't know what to do, so she called the   83
fire department. Soon fire fighters were on the scene   92
with their tall ladders. After much work, they got   101
Ebony out of the tree and into Jessie's arms.   110

"Well, I guess I won't be entering you in the   120
cat show," said Jessie. "But you sure put on a   130
spectacular show for the neighbors."   135

Oral Reading Fluency Rubric

	Rubric Score	Comments:
Phrasing and Fluency	1 2 3 4	
Intonation		
Comprehension		

Rubric Score Key
1 and 2: Student has not achieved an appropriate level of fluency for the level of the passage.
3: Fluent reading is being refined at the level of the passage.
4: Fluent reading has been achieved for the level at which the passage is written.

The Cat Show

"I am going to enter Ebony in the big cat show,   11
but first I have to give her a bath," said Jessie.   22

Ebony sensed that she was about to get a bath and   32
scrambled up a tall cottonwood tree. Jessie pleaded   40
and pleaded for her to come down. But Ebony just   49
sat high up in the tree, ignoring Jessie's pleas. All the   59
neighbors came out and tried to help   69
Jessie get Ebony down.   73

Jessie didn't know what to do, so she called the   83
fire department. Soon fire fighters were on the scene   92
with their tall ladders. After much work, they got   101
Ebony out of the tree and into Jessie's arms.   110

"Well, I guess I won't be entering you in the   120
cat show," said Jessie. "But you sure put on a   130
spectacular show for the neighbors."   135

Self-Check

1. Who are the main characters in the story?

2. Why did the cat run up the tree?

3. How did Jessie get the cat down from the tree?

4. What was the spectacular cat show in the story?

1. Jessie and Ebony are the main characters.
2. The cat ran up the tree so she could avoid getting a bath.
3. She called the fire department.
4. Getting Ebony out of the tree was the story's spectacular show.

Name: _____ Date: _____

Correct Words per Minute: _____ National Norm of Words per Minute: _____

The Rescue

6 "We'll have to wait for the
12 river to go down before we
15 cross," warned Mom.

19 "Look, the river's rising,
25 and the water is getting near
30 the cabin," Jordan alerted the
31 family.

36 As the water continued to
41 rise, Dad and Mom became
46 even more worried. They told
52 Jordan and me to pack up
57 and prepare to abandon the
62 cabin. Dad then called the
66 forest headquarters on his
68 cell phone.

73 "The ranger told me that

78 we should get to higher
83 ground because the river will
88 crest in about two hours,"
90 said Dad.

96 But it was too late. The
101 river had flowed over its
106 banks and there was no
110 escape route. We climbed
115 onto the cabin roof and
120 hoped the cabin would not
122 float away.

127 We survived the night on
132 the roof. The next morning
138 we were relieved to hear the
143 sound of a rescue helicopter
145 hovering overhead.

Oral Reading Fluency Rubric

	Rubric Score	Comments:
Phrasing and Fluency	1 2 3 4	
Intonation		
Comprehension		

Rubric Score Key

1 and 2: Student has not achieved an appropriate level of fluency for the level of the passage.

3: Fluent reading is being refined at the level of the passage.

4: Fluent reading has been achieved for the level at which the passage is written.

The Rescue

6   "We'll have to wait for the
12   river to go down before we
15   cross," warned Mom.

19   "Look, the river's rising,
25   and the water is getting near
30   the cabin," Jordan alerted the
31   family.

36   As the water continued to
41   rise, Dad and Mom became
46   even more worried. They told
52   Jordan and me to pack up
57   and prepare to abandon the
62   cabin. Dad then called the
66   forest headquarters on his
68   cell phone.

73   "The ranger told me that
78   we should get to higher

83   ground because the river will
88   crest in about two hours,"
90   said Dad.

96   But it was too late. The
101   river had flowed over its
106   banks and there was no
110   escape route. We climbed
115   onto the cabin roof and
120   hoped the cabin would not
122   float away.

127   We survived the night
132   on the roof. The next morning
138   we were relieved to hear the
143   sound of a rescue helicopter
145   hovering overhead.

Self-Check

1. What is the setting of the story?

2. Why did the family climb onto the roof?

3. What caused them to be relieved the next morning?

4. How did Dad know the river would crest?

1. The setting of the story is the family cabin by a river.
2. The escape route was flooded and they had nowhere else to go to escape the floodwaters.
3. A rescue helicopter hovering overhead made the family feel relief.
4. The ranger told Dad the river would crest.

One-Minute Oral Reading Fluency Assessment Record Form • Level R

Name: _____   Date: _____

Correct Words per Minute: _____   National Norm of Words per Minute: _____

The Talking Dogfish

5   Benson was a nosy guy

10   and was always looking for

15   interesting stories to write in

18   the school newspaper.

22   "What are you doing,

25   Martha?" asked Benson,

29   looking over his neighbor's

30   fence.

35   Martha was just sitting by

38   the garden pond.

43   "Go away, Benson. It's top

49   secret, and I don't want you

54   or anyone else to know

58   about it," said Martha.

62   "Oh, have you found

65   something interesting for

71   me to report in the school

74   newspaper?" inquired Benson.

78   Martha thought for a

82   minute, then smiled and

88   said, "Don't tell, but there's a

92   talking dogfish from Planet

98   Dingo in the pond. It was

102 delivered in this spaceship."

106 Just then Martha pulled

111 out a shiny silver machine

116 used to clean the garden

117 pond.

121 The following day, Benson's

125 newspaper report made the

129 front page: "Talking Dogfish

134 From Planet Dingo Lands in

136 Garden Pond!"

140 Benson had forgotten that

146 it was April Fools' Day, so

152 he didn't know the joke was

154 on him!

Oral Reading Fluency Rubric

	Rubric Score	Comments:
Phrasing and Fluency	1 2 3 4	
Intonation		
Comprehension		

Rubric Score Key

1 and 2: Student has not achieved an appropriate level of fluency for the level of the passage.

3: Fluent reading is being refined at the level of the passage.

4: Fluent reading has been achieved for the level at which the passage is written.

The Talking Dogfish

5 Benson was a nosy guy
10 and was always looking for
15 interesting stories to write in
18 the school newspaper.

22 "What are you doing,
25 Martha?" asked Benson,
29 looking over his neighbor's
30 fence.

35 Martha was just sitting by
38 the garden pond.

43 "Go away, Benson. It's top
49 secret, and I don't want you
54 or anyone else to know
58 about it," said Martha.

62 "Oh, have you found
65 something interesting for
71 me to report in the school
74 newspaper?" inquired Benson.

78 Martha thought for a
82 minute, then smiled and
88 said, "Don't tell, but there's a
92 talking dogfish from Planet
98 Dingo in the pond. It was
102 delivered in this spaceship."

106 Just then Martha pulled
111 out a shiny silver machine
116 used to clean the garden
117 pond.

121 The following day, Benson's
125 newspaper report made the
129 front page: "Talking Dogfish
134 From Planet Dingo Lands in
136 Garden Pond!"

140 Benson had forgotten that
146 it was April Fools' Day, so
152 he didn't know the joke was
154 on him!

Self-Check

1. Who is the main character in the story?

2. Why was Benson so nosy?

3. What did Martha tell Benson was in her pond?

4. Why was Martha playing a joke on Benson?

4. It was April Fools' Day.

3. Martha told Benson there was a talking dogfish in her pond.

2. He was a reporter for the school paper and always looking for an interesting story.

1. The main character is Benson.

Name: _____   Date: _____

Correct Words per Minute: _____   National Norm of Words per Minute: _____

The Garage Sale

5 "OK, everybody, we have too
11 much stuff we never use. I'm
15 declaring this week family
20 clean-up week," said Ryan's dad.
26 "I want everyone to scour the
31 house and collect anything you
38 haven't used in the past year. On
44 Saturday we're going to have a
49 gigantic garage sale, and the
54 proceeds will be split evenly
57 among the family."

63 Ryan sorted through the stuff in
69 his room and found many things
76 that he didn't play with or wear
81 anymore. His sister found even
87 more stuff than Ryan did to
92 contribute to the garage sale.

97 Saturday soon came, and early
102 in the morning, people began
108 arriving like a swarm of locusts
112 descending on a cornfield.

120 "It looks as if our old junk is
124 everyone else's treasure," said
129 Ryan as people purchased their
130 stuff.

134 "Yes, selling your throwaways
140 has been my pleasure!" said Dad
148 as he gave Ryan his share of the
149 proceeds.

154 "And buying new treasure with
160 the proceeds will be my pleasure!"
163 said Ryan, smiling.

Oral Reading Fluency Rubric

	Rubric Score	Comments:
Phrasing and Fluency	1 2 3 4	
Intonation		
Comprehension		

Rubric Score Key
1 and 2: Student has not achieved an appropriate level of fluency for the level of the passage.

3: Fluent reading is being refined at the level of the passage.

4: Fluent reading has been achieved for the level at which the passage is written.

The Garage Sale

5   "OK, everybody, we have too
11 much stuff we never use. I'm
15 declaring this week family
20 clean-up week," said Ryan's dad.
26 "I want everyone to scour the
31 house and collect anything you
38 haven't used in the past year. On
44 Saturday we're going to have a
49 gigantic garage sale, and the
54 proceeds will be split evenly
57 among the family."

63   Ryan sorted through the stuff in
69 his room and found many things
76 that he didn't play with or wear
81 anymore. His sister found even
87 more stuff than Ryan did to
92 contribute to the garage sale.

97   Saturday soon came, and early
102 in the morning, people began
108 arriving like a swarm of locusts
112 descending on a cornfield.

120   "It looks as if our old junk is
124 everyone else's treasure," said
129 Ryan as people purchased their
130 stuff.

134   "Yes, selling your throwaways
140 has been my pleasure!" said Dad
148 as he gave Ryan his share of the
149 proceeds.

154   "And buying new treasure with
160 the proceeds will be my pleasure!"
163 said Ryan, smiling.

Self-Check

1. What is the problem presented in the story?

2. How was the problem resolved?

3. How did the family split the proceeds from the garage sale?

4. What did Ryan do with his share of the proceeds?

1. The problem is that the family had too much unused stuff in the house.
2. The family had a garage sale.
3. Proceeds were split evenly among family members.
4. He spent it on more stuff.

One-Minute Oral Reading Fluency Assessment Record Form • Level T

Name: _____ Date: _____

Correct Words per Minute: _____ National Norm of Words per Minute: _____

The Pesky Flies

6   It was a particularly bad year

13   for flies, and they were always in

15   Justin's face.

22   "Let's buy some fly spray to get

28   rid of these pesky flies," suggested

29   Justin.

34   But his parents reminded him

41   that while fly spray might kill the

48   flies, it was also harmful to the

53   environment. So Justin began to

56   think about alternatives.

64   "I saw a man on TV wearing a

70   hat with corks dangling on strings

76   that kept flies away," said Justin.

81   "We'd look silly wearing hats

88   like that to work, school, and the

92   mall," protested Justin's mom.

98   "Hey, frogs eat pesky flies, and

105   we could raise frogs in our house,"

107   suggested Justin.

114   "I don't think it would be fair

123   to force frogs to live in tanks in our

127   house," objected Justin's dad.

131   Justin thought harder and

137   suddenly blurted out, "Oh, I know

143   something that'll get rid of the

151   flies. It's green like a frog and it

154   'eats' flies, too."

160   "A green spider or a green

164   vacuum cleaner?" responded his

165   mom.

169   "No, green Venus flytraps love

174   eating pesky flies!" said Justin.

Oral Reading Fluency Rubric

	Rubric Score	Comments:
Phrasing and Fluency	1 2 3 4	
Intonation		
Comprehension		

Rubric Score Key

1 and 2: Student has not achieved an appropriate level of fluency for the level of the passage.

3: Fluent reading is being refined at the level of the passage.

4: Fluent reading has been achieved for the level at which the passage is written.

The Pesky Flies

6　　　It was a particularly bad year
13　for flies, and they were always in
15　Justin's face.

22　　　"Let's buy some fly spray to get
28　rid of these pesky flies," suggested
29　Justin.

34　　　But his parents reminded him
41　that while fly spray might kill the
48　flies, it was also harmful to the
53　environment. So Justin began to
56　think about alternatives.

64　　　"I saw a man on TV wearing a
70　hat with corks dangling on strings
76　that kept flies away," said Justin.

81　　　"We'd look silly wearing hats
88　like that to work, school, and the
92　mall," protested Justin's mom.

98　　　"Hey, frogs eat pesky flies, and
105　we could raise frogs in our house,"
107　suggested Justin.

114　　　"I don't think it would be fair to
123　force frogs to live in tanks in our
127　house," objected Justin's dad.

131　　　Justin thought harder and
137　suddenly blurted out, "Oh, I know
143　something that'll get rid of the
151　flies. It's green like a frog and it
154　'eats' flies, too."

160　　　"A green spider or a green
164　vacuum cleaner?" responded his
165　mom.

169　　　"No, green Venus flytraps love
174　eating pesky flies!" said Justin.

Self-Check

1. What is the setting of the story?

2. What is the problem?

3. What was wrong with using fly spray to get rid of the flies?

4. How did Justin resolve the problem?

1. The setting of the story is Justin's house.
2. The problem is that there were too many pesky flies.
3. It was harmful to the environment.
4. He suggested getting Venus flytraps, which would eat the flies.

One-Minute Oral Reading Fluency Assessment Record Form • Level U

Name: _____ Date: _____

Correct Words per Minute: _____ National Norm of Words per Minute: _____

Land Sailing

5	Most weekends, Lara and her
12	family go land sailing on the dry
17	lakebed in a nearby desert.
21	"Remember your helmet and
26	gloves, Lara. You got enormous
32	blisters and rope burns on your
38	hands when you last went land
42	sailing without gloves," said
44	her dad.
49	Mom limped toward the car
53	holding a black-and-white checked
60	flag. She severely injured her leg in
66	a racing accident four years before,
72	so instead of racing, she now
79	waves the flag as the winners cross
82	the finish line.
89	"I'm going to see if I can
95	improve on my speed record from

last weekend by at least a few	**102**
miles per hour," said Lara's	**107**
brother, Reggie.	**109**
"I'm going to practice my	**114**
favorite trick—lifting one side of	**120**
my dirtboat off the ground while	**126**
zooming along on just two	**131**
wheels," said Lara.	**134**
"You kids are speedsters and	**139**
tricksters, just like your mom,"	**144**
said Dad.	**146**
"You were the national dirtboat	**151**
champion for two years in a row,	**158**
Dad, so I think we take after you!"	**166**
said Reggie.	**168**
"Yes, but your mother taught	**173**
me everything I know about	**178**
dirtboats!" said Dad, laughing.	**182**

Oral Reading Fluency Rubric

	Rubric Score	Comments:
Phrasing and Fluency	1 2 3 4	
Intonation		
Comprehension		

Rubric Score Key

1 and 2: Student has not achieved an appropriate level of fluency for the level of the passage.

3: Fluent reading is being refined at the level of the passage.

4: Fluent reading has been achieved for the level at which the passage is written.

Informal Assessments for Fluency Development

Land Sailing

5   Most weekends, Lara and her
12   family go land sailing on the dry
17   lakebed in a nearby desert.
21   "Remember your helmet and
26   gloves, Lara. You got enormous
32   blisters and rope burns on your
38   hands when you last went land
42   sailing without gloves," said
44   her dad.
49   Mom limped toward the car
53   holding a black-and-white checked
60   flag. She severely injured her leg in
66   a racing accident four years before,
72   so instead of racing, she now waves
79   the flag as the winners cross the
82   finish line.
89   "I'm going to see if I can
95   improve on my speed record from

last weekend by at least a few miles   102
per hour," said Lara's   107
brother, Reggie.   109
     "I'm going to practice my   114
favorite trick—lifting one side of   120
my dirtboat off the ground while   126
zooming along on just two wheels,"   131
said Lara.   134
     "You kids are speedsters and   139
tricksters, just like your mom,"   144
said Dad.   146
     "You were the national dirtboat   151
champion for two years in a row,   158
Dad, so I think we take after you!"   166
said Reggie.   168
     "Yes, but your mother taught   173
me everything I know about   178
dirtboats!" said Dad, laughing.   182

Self-Check

1. What activity does the family in the story enjoy?

2. Where does the activity take place?

3. How has Lara's mom's involvement in the activity changed since her accident?

4. Why does Lara's dad call her and her brother tricksters and speedsters?

1. The family enjoys land sailing, or dirtboarding.
2. The activity takes place at a dried-up lakebed.
3. She now waves a black-and-white checked flag at the finish line rather than racing a dirtboat.
4. Lara and her brother like to go fast and do tricks.

Name: _____ Date: _____

Correct Words per Minute: _____ National Norm of Words per Minute: _____

Nebulas, Where Stars Are Born

9	No matter what class a star is, all stars
18	are born in the same way. They all begin
23	in a nebula (NEH-byuh-luh). This is
32	a thick cloud of gas and dust in space.
37	Nebulas contain mainly hydrogen gas
44	and a small amount of helium gas.
50	There are different types of nebulas.
56	Emission nebulas give off light. A
63	reflection nebula reflects the light of stars
69	around it. Planetary nebulas are formed
77	when a sun-sized star dies and sheds its
84	outer layers. A dark nebula is comprised
94	of so much dust and gas that it blocks out
98	all light around it.
104	Dark nebula clouds are often very
110	large, spanning across many millions of
116	miles. And yet, astronomers believe that
122	stars are born inside these nebulas.

Inside the dark nebula, gas and dust	129
stick together and form clumps. A large	136
clump has more gravity. This gravity can	143
pull other particles of gas and dust to the	152
clump. With more particles, the clump	158
increases in mass. Mass is the amount of	166
matter that something contains.	170
The gravity continues to pull the	176
particles very close together. Sometimes a	182
nearby star explodes and sends out shock	189
waves. The shock waves can push the gas	197
and dust particles even closer together.	203
The thickly-packed gas and dust	208
create a very hot, dense space in the	216
center of the clump. Eventually this core	223
will vaporize the dust. Then, the nebula	230
collapses. The collapse of a nebula is the	238
beginning of a star's birth.	243

Oral Reading Fluency Rubric

	Rubric Score	Comments:
Phrasing and Fluency	1 2 3 4	
Intonation		
Comprehension		

Rubric Score Key

1 and 2: Student has not achieved an appropriate level of fluency for the level of the passage.

3: Fluent reading is being refined at the level of the passage.

4: Fluent reading has been achieved for the level at which the passage is written.

Nebulas, Where Stars Are Born

9   No matter what class a star is, all stars

18   are born in the same way. They all begin

23   in a nebula (NEH-byuh-luh). This is

32   a thick cloud of gas and dust in space.

37   Nebulas contain mainly hydrogen gas

44   and a small amount of helium gas.

50   There are different types of nebulas.

56   Emission nebulas give off light. A

63   reflection nebula reflects the light of stars

69   around it. Planetary nebulas are formed

77   when a sun-sized star dies and sheds its

84   outer layers. A dark nebula is comprised

94   of so much dust and gas that it blocks out

98   all light around it.

104   Dark nebula clouds are often very

110   large, spanning across many millions of

116   miles. And yet, astronomers believe that

122   stars are born inside these nebulas.

Inside the dark nebula, gas and dust 129

stick together and form clumps. A large 136

clump has more gravity. This gravity can 143

pull other particles of gas and dust to the 152

clump. With more particles, the clump 158

increases in mass. Mass is the amount of 166

matter that something contains. 170

The gravity continues to pull the 176

particles very close together. Sometimes a 182

nearby star explodes and sends out shock 189

waves. The shock waves can push the gas 197

and dust particles even closer together. 203

The thickly-packed gas and dust 208

create a very hot, dense space in the 216

center of the clump. Eventually this core 223

will vaporize the dust. Then, the nebula 230

collapses. The collapse of a nebula is the 238

beginning of a star's birth. 243

Self-Check ✔

1. What is a nebula?

2. What are the different types of nebulas?

3. Does a small clump pull more or fewer particles than a large clump? How do you know?

4. What are the important ideas in this passage?

1. A nebula is a thick cloud of gas and dust in space.

2. The different types of nebulas are emissions nebulas, planetary nebulas, and dark nebulas.

3. A small clump pulls fewer particles because it has less gravity.

4. The important ideas in the passage are
- all stars begin in nebulas,
- gas and particles clump together inside nebulas,
- the core of a nebula gets very dense and very hot,
- a star is born when a nebula collapses.

Name: _____ Date: _____

Correct Words per Minute: _____ National Norm of Words per Minute: _____

The Chernobyl Disaster

4   At 11 P.M. on April 25, 1986, nuclear

8   (NOO-klee-er) power plant workers in

11   Ukraine (yoo-KRANE) began running

17   a test on a reactor (ree-AK-ter). That's

23   the equipment that splits atoms without

32   causing an explosion. The test did not go as

33   planned.

37   About 1:23 A.M. on April 26, two

41   explosions rocked the Chernobyl-4

44   (cher-NOH-bul) reactor. Workers did

50   not realize how horrible the situation

58   was. People in nearby villages had no idea

65   that their lives had just been changed

66   forever.

72   During the testing at Chernobyl, the

77   splitting atoms overheated. The whole

85   process went too fast. Water in the reactor

91   turned into too much steam. Steam

99   pressure blew the lid off the reactor. The

104   shield that kept the radioactive (ray-dee-

110   oh-AK-tiv) materials in the reactor flew off.

116   Burning radioactive material burst out and

123   formed a cloud. Larger chunks of material

126   started several fires.

132   No one realized how much radioactive

139   material they were breathing in, or how

146   much was getting on their skin. Brave

154   people fought the fires. They saved the rest

160   of the plant from catching fire.

166   Many of the firefighters and workers

172   died or later had serious illnesses.

176   After the explosion, about 135,000

182   people had to leave their homes

188   permanently. The land and water were

195   terribly toxic. Villages as far as 20 miles (32

201   kilometers) away were no longer livable.

Oral Reading Fluency Rubric

	Rubric Score	Comments:
Phrasing and Fluency	1 2 3 4	
Intonation		
Comprehension		

Rubric Score Key

1 and 2: Student has not achieved an appropriate level of fluency for the level of the passage.

3: Fluent reading is being refined at the level of the passage.

4: Fluent reading has been achieved for the level at which the passage is written.

The Chernobyl Disaster

4   At 11 P.M. on April 25, 1986, nuclear

8   (NOO-klee-er) power plant workers in

11 Ukraine (yoo-KRANE) began running

17 a test on a reactor (ree-AK-ter). That's

23 the equipment that splits atoms without

32 causing an explosion. The test did not go as

33 planned.

37   About 1:23 A.M. on April 26, two

41 explosions rocked the Chernobyl-4

44 (cher-NOH-bul) reactor. Workers did

50 not realize how horrible the situation

58 was. People in nearby villages had no idea

65 that their lives had just been changed

66 forever.

72   During the testing at Chernobyl, the

77 splitting atoms overheated. The whole

85 process went too fast. Water in the reactor

91 turned into too much steam. Steam

99 pressure blew the lid off the reactor. The

104 shield that kept the radioactive (ray-dee-

110 oh-AK-tiv) materials in the reactor flew off.

116 Burning radioactive material burst out and

123 formed a cloud. Larger chunks of material

126 started several fires.

132   No one realized how much radioactive

139 material they were breathing in, or how

146 much was getting on their skin. Brave

154 people fought the fires. They saved the rest

160 of the plant from catching fire.

166   Many of the firefighters and workers

172 died or later had serious illnesses.

176   After the explosion, about 135,000

182 people had to leave their homes

188 permanently. The land and water were

195 terribly toxic. Villages as far as 20 miles (32

201 kilometers) away were no longer livable.

Self-Check

1. What is a reactor?

2. What started fires?

3. How did the events of April 26, 1986 affect the way people felt about living near nuclear power plants?

4. What happens to people when they come into contact with radioactive material?

1. A reactor is the equipment that splits atoms without causing an explosion.
2. Large chunks of burning radioactive material started fires.
3. People didn't want to live near nuclear power plants because they were afraid of disasters like the one that happened at Chernobyl.
4. People can get sick when people come into contact with burning radioactive material.

One-Minute Oral Reading Fluency Assessment Record Form • Level X

Name: _____   Date: _____

Correct Words per Minute: _____   National Norm of Words per Minute: _____

Volcanoes: Nature's Awesome Power

8   A volcano is any opening on Earth where

15   material from inside the planet—molten rock,

24   debris, and steam—makes its way to the surface.

31   What causes a volcanic eruption? Volcanoes erupt

39   when pressures within Earth force magma to the

46   surface. Magma collects deep underground in a

53   magma chamber. Under pressure, the magma rises

62   and bursts through the crust in weak spots called

69   vents. When pressure on the magma subsides,

79   the eruption stops. This is much like a tube of

86   toothpaste that you squeeze. The harder you

94   squeeze, the more toothpaste squirts out. When you

100   stop squeezing, you stop the flow.

108   Three kinds of materials may erupt from a

115   volcano: lava, tephra (rock fragments), and gases.

125   Lava is magma that has reached the surface of a

129   volcano. The terms pahoehoe (pah-HOH-ee-hoh-ee)

136   and aa (AH-ah) are Hawaiian words that describe

147   the lava flow. Aa is thick. Like honey or molasses, it

156   flows slowly down the slopes. Pahoehoe is thin and

163   flows more quickly. When pahoehoe first erupts,

173   get out of the way. This lava can outrun you!

180   All volcanoes release gases during an eruption.

190   The pressure of the gas in the magma causes the

200   eruption. Some volcanoes erupt with more than

207   just lava. If the magma contains a lot of gas,

217   it will burst out violently with rock fragments

225   called pyroclastic (PY-roh-KLAS-tik) materials.

228   The pressure of the gas sends fragments of rock

237   blasting out of the volcano. Some volcanoes

244   alternate between eruptions of lava and eruptions of

246   pyroclastic materials.

253   Sometimes a tall column of pyroclastic materials

263   and gases collapses. It races down the slope of the

272   volcano at dangerous speeds in what is called a

281   pyroclastic flow. The speed of these flows can reach

284   120 miles per hour!

292   When a volcano erupts, it can spew out

301   anything from fine particles of dust to huge blocks

308   of rock as big as a house.

Oral Reading Fluency Rubric

	Rubric Score				Comments:
Phrasing and Fluency	1	2	3	4	
Intonation					
Comprehension					

Rubric Score Key

1 and 2: Student has not achieved an appropriate level of fluency for the level of the passage.

3: Fluent reading is being refined at the level of the passage.

4: Fluent reading has been achieved for the level at which the passage is written.

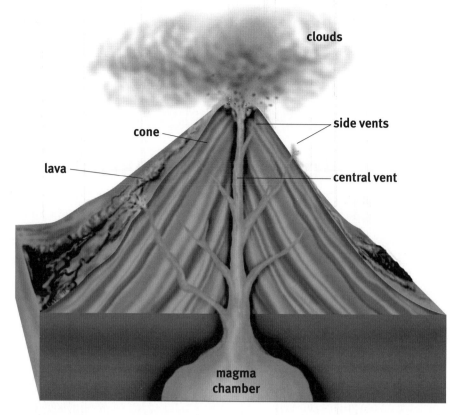

cone

lava

clouds

side vents

central vent

magma chamber

diagram of a volcanic eruption

Volcanoes: Nature's Awesome Power

8 A volcano is any opening on Earth where
15 material from inside the planet—molten rock,
24 debris, and steam—makes its way to the surface.
31 What causes a volcanic eruption? Volcanoes erupt
39 when pressures within Earth force magma to the
46 surface. Magma collects deep underground in a
53 magma chamber. Under pressure, the magma rises
62 and bursts through the crust in weak spots called
69 vents. When pressure on the magma subsides,
79 the eruption stops. This is much like a tube of
86 toothpaste that you squeeze. The harder you
94 squeeze, the more toothpaste squirts out. When you
100 stop squeezing, you stop the flow.

108 Three kinds of materials may erupt from a
115 volcano: lava, tephra (rock fragments), and gases.
125 Lava is magma that has reached the surface of a
129 volcano. The terms pahoehoe (pah-HOH-ee-hoh-ee)
136 and aa (AH-ah) are Hawaiian words that describe
147 the lava flow. Aa is thick. Like honey or molasses, it
156 flows slowly down the slopes. Pahoehoe is thin and

163 flows more quickly. When pahoehoe first erupts,
173 get out of the way. This lava can outrun you!

180 All volcanoes release gases during an eruption.
190 The pressure of the gas in the magma causes the
200 eruption. Some volcanoes erupt with more than
207 just lava. If the magma contains a lot of gas,
217 it will burst out violently with rock fragments
225 called pyroclastic (PY-roh-KLAS-tik) materials.
228 The pressure of the gas sends fragments of rock
237 blasting out of the volcano. Some volcanoes
244 alternate between eruptions of lava and eruptions of
246 pyroclastic materials.

253 Sometimes a tall column of pyroclastic materials
263 and gases collapses. It races down the slope of the
272 volcano at dangerous speeds in what is called a
281 pyroclastic flow. The speed of these flows can reach
284 120 miles per hour!

292 When a volcano erupts, it can spew out
301 anything from fine particles of dust to huge blocks
308 of rock as big as a house.

Informal Assessments for Fluency Development
©2011 Benchmark Education Company, LLC

Self-Check

1. What is a volcano?

2. What types of materials erupt from a volcano?

3. What is this passage mainly about?

4. Describe the temperature inside a volcano.

1. A volcano is any opening on Earth where material inside the planet makes its way to the surface.
2. Lava, tephra, and gases erupt from a volcano.
3. This passage is mostly about the force behind a volcanic eruption.
4. The temperature inside a volcano is very hot. It is hot enough to melt rock.

"Assessing metacognition allows us to discover students' perceptions of themselves as readers and writers, the reading and writing they do, and the strategies they employ to solve the problems they encounter in reading and writing."

—Rhodes & Shanklin, 1993

Fluency Self-Assessment Checklist

The Fluency Self-Assessment Checklist can be used with students of all ages to promote reflection and goal setting for improving fluent reading. Younger students can use the form with happy/sad faces and older students the yes/no response version. These same prompts can be used as you conduct individual reading conferences with students as prompts for student reflection and evaluation of their reading performance. After completing the self-assessment, students can use the checklist to identify areas in need of reinforcement and set goals for improving the various aspects of fluency including speed/pacing, pausing, inflection/intonation, phrasing, expression, and integration of accuracy, rate, and prosody. Discuss with students the connection between how they read a particular text and the impact on comprehension.

Name: _____ Date: _____

Fluency Self-Assessment Master Checklist

☺ ☹

Speed/Pacing
Did my speed and pacing match the kind of text I was reading? ☐ ☐
Did my speed and pacing match what the author was saying? ☐ ☐
Did I read in a natural talking sound? ☐ ☐
Did I slow my reading down when appropriate? ☐ ☐
Did I pay attention to punctuation? ☐ ☐

Pausing
Did I pause to keep from running all my words together? ☐ ☐
Did I pause in the correct locations? ☐ ☐
Did I pause for the appropriate length of time? ☐ ☐
Did I pause to help my reading make sense? ☐ ☐
Did I use punctuation to help me figure out when to pause? ☐ ☐

Inflection/Intonation
Did I make my voice rise at a question mark? ☐ ☐
Did I make my voice fall at a period? ☐ ☐
Did I think about what the author was saying so I would
know when to read louder or softer? ☐ ☐
Did I think about what the author was saying so I would know
when to stress or emphasize words? ☐ ☐

Phrasing
Did I notice the phrases? ☐ ☐
Did I read all the words in each phrase together? ☐ ☐
Did I think about what the words in the phrase mean when
they are together? ☐ ☐

Expression
Did I look for clues so I could anticipate the mood of the passage? ☐ ☐
Did I use my tone of voice, facial expressions, and body language
to express what the author or characters were thinking or feeling? ☐ ☐
Did I change my reading when something new was about to happen? ☐ ☐

Integration
Did I read the words right? (accuracy) ☐ ☐
Did I read the words at the right speed? (rate) ☐ ☐
Did I read with expression? (prosody) ☐ ☐
Did my reading sound like talking? ☐ ☐
Did I understand what I read? ☐ ☐

Name: _____ Date: _____

Fluency Self-Assessment Master Checklist

	Yes	No
Speed/Pacing		
Did my speed and pacing match the kind of text I was reading?	❑	❑
Did my speed and pacing match what the author was saying?	❑	❑
Did I read in a natural talking sound?	❑	❑
Did I slow my reading down when appropriate?	❑	❑
Did I pay attention to punctuation?	❑	❑
Pausing		
Did I pause to keep from running all my words together?	❑	❑
Did I pause in the correct locations?	❑	❑
Did I pause for the appropriate length of time?	❑	❑
Did I pause to help my reading make sense?	❑	❑
Did I use punctuation to help me figure out when to pause?	❑	❑
Inflection/Intonation		
Did I make my voice rise at a question mark?	❑	❑
Did I make my voice fall at a period?	❑	❑
Did I think about what the author was saying so I would know when to read louder or softer?	❑	❑
Did I think about what the author was saying so I would know when to stress or emphasize words?	❑	❑
Phrasing		
Did I notice the phrases?	❑	❑
Did I read all the words in each phrase together?	❑	❑
Did I think about what the words in the phrase mean when they are together?	❑	❑
Expression		
Did I look for clues so I could anticipate the mood of the passage?	❑	❑
Did I use my tone of voice, facial expressions, and body language to express what the author or characters were thinking or feeling?	❑	❑
Did I change my reading when something new was about to happen?	❑	❑
Integration		
Did I read the words right? (accuracy)	❑	❑
Did I read the words at the right speed? (rate)	❑	❑
Did I read with expression? (prosody)	❑	❑
Did my reading sound like talking?	❑	❑
Did I understand what I read?	❑	❑

Reader's Theater and oral presentations provide opportunities for students to model fluent reading. Rubrics and checklists can be used before, during, and after performances to improve fluency and to help students prepare for final public performances.

Reader's Theater Assessment Rubric

Use the Reader's Theater Assessment Rubric during individual conferences or after a performance to assess students' understanding of characterization. The rubric includes a rating scale for assessing the following:

Phrasing and Fluency

Expression, Intonation, and Volume

Pace

Accuracy

Characterization

Listening

Behavior

Reader's Theater Assessment Rubric

Rating Scale	Phrasing and Fluency
1	Reads word by word. Does not attend to the author's syntax or sentence structures.
2	Reads slowly and in a choppy manner, usually in two-word phrases. Some attention is given to the author's syntax and sentence structures.
3	Reads in phrases of three or four words. Appropriate syntax is used.
4	Reads in longer, more meaningful phrases. Regularly uses pitch, stress, and author's syntax to reflect comprehension.
	Intonation
1	Reads with a monotone voice.
2	Reads with some intonation and some attention to punctuation. At times reads in a monotone voice.
3	Reads by adjusting intonation appropriately. Consistently attends to punctuation.
4	Reads with intonation that reflects feeling, anticipation, tension, character development, and mood.
	Listening
1	Does not listen attentively and cannot provide relevant suggestions to improve readings of others. Is disruptive.
2	Listens most of the time but has difficulty commenting on the readings of others.
3	Listens to the readings of others without interruption. Makes some suggestions for ways to improve readings. Needs help clarifying own ideas and ideas of others.
4	Listens to the readings of others without interruption. Comments positively on the readings and makes appropriate suggestions for improvement. Seeks clarification when something is not understood. Clarifies own comments when not understood by others, using such phrasing as "what I meant was…"
	Pace
1	Slow and laborious reading.
2	Reading is either moderately slow or inappropriately fast.
3	Unbalanced combination of slow and fast reading.
4	Reading is consistently natural, conversational, and appropriate (resembling natural oral language).

Reader's Theater Assessment Rubric

Rating Scale	Accuracy
1	Multiple attempts at decoding words without success. Word reading accuracy is inadequate/poor (below 85%).
2	Attempts to self-correct errors, usually unsuccessful. Word reading accuracy is marginal (between 86%–90%).
3	Attempts to self-correct errors are successful. Word reading accuracy is good (between 91%–95%).
4	Most words are read correctly on initial attempt. Minimal self-corrections, all successful. Word reading accuracy is excellent (96% and above).
	Characterization
1	Has difficulty understanding the characters and cannot portray them accurately.
2	Can characterize accurately those characters presented in a straightforward way but has difficulty making inferences, even with teacher guidance.
3	Can characterize accurately those characters presented in a straightforward way. With teacher guidance, can understand more subtle characteristics and make inferences about characters in a given situation.
4	Makes accurate inferences and interpretations about characters, using appropriate voice, tone, expression, and body language.
	Behavior
1	Cannot work independently when others are rehearsing or working with the teacher. When in a group situation, needs continual reminders of rehearsal and performance expectations. Has difficulty working with other students: doesn't take turns, speaks at inappropriate times, doesn't listen, is disruptive and distracting.
2	Tries to work independently, but is occasionally disruptive. Sometimes forgets rehearsal and performance expectations. Has some difficulty working with others.
3	Usually works quietly and responsibly when others are rehearsing. Understands expectations and follows through most of the time. Usually works well with others.
4	Works quietly and responsibly on independent activities when others are rehearsing or working with the teacher. Understands rehearsal and performance expectations and acts on them. Works well with others.

Reader's Theater Self-Assessment (Levels A–E)

Name: _____ Date: _____

After a Reader's Theater performance, ask students to use the Self-Assessment form (appropriate for their level) to monitor and evaluate their reading and performance of a script.

1. Did your reading sound like talking?
   ☺   😐   ☹

2. Did you use your voice to show the character's feelings?
   ☺   😐   ☹

3. Did you say the lines like the characters would say them?
   ☺   😐   ☹

4. Did you use the punctuation marks to help you know how to say the words?
   ☺   😐   ☹

5. Did you read with a good speed?
   ☺   😐   ☹

6. Did you fix your mistakes when you read?
   ☺   😐   ☹

7. Did you act like your character?
   ☺   😐   ☹

8. Did you listen carefully to the other readers?
   ☺   😐   ☹

Reader's Theater Self-Assessment (Levels F–M)

Student: _____ Script: _____

Character I Portray: _____ Date: _____

Please read each item and think about how fluently you read the character's lines. Place a mark next to either **yes** or **no** on the lines provided. Talk to your teacher about items you need more help with in rehearsal.

Did I make my reading sound like talking? _____ **yes** _____ **no**

Did I read in phrases? _____ **yes** _____ **no**

Did I use my voice to show the character's feelings? _____ **yes** _____ **no**

Did I say the lines like the character would? _____ **yes** _____ **no**

Did my voice change to show that I read the punctuation marks? _____ **yes** _____ **no**

Did I read with a good speed? _____ **yes** _____ **no**

Did I fix my mistakes when I read? _____ **yes** _____ **no**

Did I act like the character? _____ **yes** _____ **no**

Reader's Theater Self-Assessment (Levels N–X)

Name: _____ Script: _____

Character I Portray: _____ Date: _____

Please read each item and think about how fluently you read the character's lines. As you read through each element of fluency, mark **yes** or **no** responses on the lines provided. At the bottom, tell how you plan to improve your reading in the areas where you answered **no**. Make comments or give examples of how well you read and list any areas where you could receive more help.

1. As I read, did I read for phrasing and fluency by:
   - reading in longer, meaningful phrases? _____
   - paying attention to the author's language patterns (words, sentences)? _____
   - making the reading sound like dialogue or natural oral language? _____
   - stressing certain words to emphasize/reveal the importance of a word or phrase? _____

2. As I read, did I read using intonation by:
   - using my voice to make the reading reflect the feelings, anticipation, tension, mood and personality of the character? _____
   - paying attention to punctuation? _____
   - interpreting the punctuation and using my voice to appropriately raise or lower its sound because of the type of sentence/punctuation I read? _____

3. As I read, did I pay attention to pace by:
   - using an appropriate speed of reading? _____
   - reading the lines with the same speed and flow that I use when I talk? _____
   - reading with very few hesitations or unnecessary pauses and repetitions? _____

4. As I read, did I read accurately by:
   - quickly recognizing words and reading them correctly? _____
   - really thinking about the meaning of the story and known words (high-frequency words, sight words, etc.) and word parts as anchors to help me figure out unknown words? _____
   - self-correcting any miscues or errors on my first try/ attempt? _____
   - making the words sound meaningful? _____

5. As I read, did I really try to understand the character and read and say the lines the same way the character probably would by:
   - making inferences about the character? _____
   - using my voice (tone) to sound like the character? _____
   - using my voice to express a particular feeling of the character? _____
   - using body language (gestures) to better express the feelings of the character? _____
   - using appropriate expressions (facial) in a way that would best represent the character? _____

Plan of Action: I will work on improving my reading fluency during the repeated readings of my character lines by:

_____

_____

_____

When reading independently, I feel...

_____

I would like my teacher or a peer to help me with...

1. _____

2. _____

3. _____

Fluency Self-Assessment

Name: _____ Date: _____

Script: _____ Role: _____

Complete the rubric below. Tell how you plan to improve your reading fluency in the areas where you answered no.

Skill	Behavior	Yes	No
Fluency and Phrasing	I read in longer, meaningful phrases.		
	I paid attention to the author's language patterns.		
	I made the reading sound like dialogue.		
	I stressed certain words to emphasize their importance.		
Intonation	I used my voice to make the reading reflect feeling, anticipation, tension, mood, and the personality of my character.		
	I paid attention to punctuation.		
	I raised or lowered my voice to interpret the punctuation of sentences.		
Pacing	I used an appropriate speed of reading.		
	I read the lines with the same speed and flow that I use when I talk.		
	I read with very few hesitations or unnecessary pauses and repetitions.		
Accuracy	I recognized words quickly and read them correctly.		
	I really thought about the meaning of the story and known words and word parts to help me figure out unknown words.		
	I corrected myself when I made an error.		
Character Analysis	I made the words sound meaningful.		
	I made inferences about my character.		
	I used my voice (tone) to sound like the character.		
	I used my voice to express a particular feeling of the character.		
	I used body language (gestures) to better express the feelings of the character.		
	I used appropriate facial expressions to represent my character.		

Plan of Action: Describe how you will improve your reading fluency during the repeated readings of your character's lines.

_____

_____

_____

Reader's Theater Performance Assessment

Name: _____ Script: _____

Character I Portray: _____ Date: _____

Use the Reader's Theater Performance Assessment to record how well students performed during a Reader's Theater presentation. Information learned can be used for goal setting by students for future performances and to inform your instruction and areas in need of support.

Skill	Bravo!	Take a Bow	Star Potential	Let's Rehearse
Shows leadership while planning and rehearsing				
Works as a team member by supporting other readers				
Speaks confidently, audibly, clearly, and expressively				
Keeps audience's attention with tone, expression, and volume of voice				
Demonstrates an understanding of the character's emotions, moods, actions, and point of view				
Reads in a style that reinforces the drama or humor of the story situation				
Adjusts pitch, stress, intonation, phrasing, and pacing to achieve desired meaning				
Uses facial expressions, body language, gestures, and movement effectively				
Picks up cues without hesitation				
Listens to and reacts appropriately to other characters' lines and actions				
Stays in character even when not reading lines				
Doesn't fidget, look around, or giggle during performance				
Effectively transitions between scenes; effectively moves on and off stage as needed				
Handles unexpected circumstances without getting ruffled				
Puts on a performance that would make the script's author smile				

Oral Presentation Rubric

Assessing oral presentations can provide opportunities to examine fluency through public speaking events. Identify how well prepared the speaker was, how well the speaker understood the subject matter, and the areas of strengths and weakness in verbal and nonverbal skills. Oral presentations provide students a forum to share understandings and build communication skills and confidence.

Oral Presentation Rubric

Name: _____ Date: _____

Presentation Title: _____ Presentation Topic: _____ Presentation Length: _____ minutes

Presentation Element	1 (Beginning)	2 (Developing)	3 (Accomplished)	4 (Exemplary)
Content				
Subject Knowledge				
Organization				
Sources				
Delivery				
Technology, Media, Graphics, Props				
Speaking (Volume, Pacing, Word Choice, Pronunciation)				
Posture and Eye Contact				
Enthusiasm				
Eye Contact				
Body Language				
Posture & Poise				
Other				
Confidence				
Preparation				
Creativity				

Informal Assessments for Fluency Development   ©2011 Benchmark Education Company, LLC

APPENDIX

Year-at-a-Glance Planning Calendar

Teacher Name: _____   Grade: _____   Level: _____

Notes:	August	September	October
November	December	January	February
March	April	May	June

Month-at-a-Glance Planning Calendar

Teacher Name: _____ Grade: _____ Level: _____

	Monday	Tuesday	Wednesday	Thursday	Friday
Week of:					
Week of:					
Week of:					
Week of:					

Week-at-a-Glance Planning Calendar

Teacher Name: _____   Grade: _____   Level: _____

	Monday	Tuesday	Wednesday	Thursday	Friday
Progress-Monitoring Assessments					
Individual Reading Conferences					

Anecdotal Notes

Teacher Name: _____

Grade: _____

Level: _____

Informal Assessments for Fluency Development

Cowie, R., Douglas-Cowie, E. & Wichmann, A. (2002). "Prosodic characteristics of skilled reading: Fluency and expressiveness in 8–10 year old readers." *Language and Speech*, 45 (1), 47–82.

Daane, M. C., Campbell, J. R. Grigg, W. S., Goodman, M.J. & Oranje, A. (2005). *Fourth-grade students reading aloud: NAEP 2002 special study of oral reading. The nation's report card* (NCES 2006-469). Washington, D. C: U. S. Department of Education, Institute of Education Sciences.

Hirschberg, J. (2002). "Communication and prosody: Functional aspects of prosody." *Speech Communication*, 10 (2), 163–169.

Klauda, S. L. & Guthrie, J. T. (2008). "Relationships of three components of reading fluency to reading comprehension." Journal of Educational Psychology, 100 (2), 310-321.

Kuhn, M. R., Schwanenflugel, P. J., Meisinger, E. B. (2010). "Aligning Theory and Assessment of Reading Fluency: Automaticy, Prosody, and Definitions of Fluency." *Reading Research Quarterly*, 45 (2), 230–251.

Logan, G. D. (1997). "Automaticity and reading: Perspectives from the instance theory of automatization." *Reading & Writing Quarterly*, 13 (2), 123–146.

McKenna, M.C. & Stahl, S. A. (2003). *Assessment for reading instruction*. New York: Guilford.

Miller, J. & Schwanenflugel, P. J. (2006). "Prosody of syntactically complex sentences in the oral reading of young children." *Journal of Educational Psychology*, 98 (4), 839–853.

Miller, J. & Schwanenflugel, P. J. (2008). "A longitudinal study of the development of reading prosody as a dimension of oral reading fluency in early elementary school children." *Reading Research Quarterly*, 43 (4), 336–354.

RAND Reading Study Group. (2002). *Reading for understanding: Toward an R & D program in reading comprehension*. Santa Monica, CA: RAND Corporation.

Rasinski, T. (2004). *Assessing reading fluency*. Honolulu, HI: Pacific Resources for Education and Learning.

Samuels, S. J. (2004). "Toward a theory of automatic information processing in reading." In R. B. Ruddell & N. J. Unrau (Eds.), *Theoretical models and processes* (1,127–1,148). Newark, DE: International Reading Association.

Samuels, S. J. (2006). "Reading Fluency: Its past, present, and future." In T. Rasinksi, C. Blachowicz, & K. Lems (Eds) *Fluency instruction: Research-based practices* (7–20). New York: Guilford.

Schwanenflugal, P. J., Hamilton, A. M., Kuhn, M. R., Wisenbaker, J. M., & Stahl, S. A. (2004). "Becoming a fluent reader: Reading skill and prosodic features in the oral reading of young readers." *Journal of Educational Psychology*, 96 (1), 119–129.

Stecker, S. K., Roser, N. L. & Martinez, M. G. (1998). "Understanding oral reading fluency." In T. Shanahan & F. V. Rodriguez-Brown (Eds.). *47th Yearbook of the National Reading Conference* (295–310). Chicago: National Reading Conference.

Wixson, K. K. & Lipson, M. Y. (2009, May). "Response to intervention: Promises, possibilities, and potential problems for reading professionals." Paper presented at the Reading Research Conference, Minneapolis, MN.

Zutell, J. & Rasinksi, T. (1991). Training teachers to attend to their students' oral reading fluency. *Theory into Practice*, 30 (3), 211–217.

NOTES:

Informal Assessments for Fluency Development

NOTES:

NOTES:

Informal Assessments for Fluency Development